The History of Water

The Sheffield Reflection

civilisation in a pipeline

by Dr. J. Stephenson

RESERVOIR OF CONTENTS

Introduction

Water is essential for life

Clean water is essential for health

This basic, readily-available everyday part of our lives is easily taken for granted, here in the developed world. History tells us that it wasn't always like this, and that behind the tap lies the convoluted story of death and destruction, endeavour and enterprise.

I realised how much we take for granted this clean health-giving supply, and the convenient, beautifully engineered toilets which we all enjoy, while I was researching the cholera outbreaks in Sheffield for my first book. Also, while reading the Report of 1847 into the 'Sanatory Condition' of Sheffield, it was brought home to me how much people suffered in those days. Their diseases and deaths were eminently preventable, by provision of clean water and the removal of all kinds of waste. Why was the evidence of the day ignored, and not acted upon as an urgent priority?

The Water Well Dressing, Litton, Derbyshire Summer 2017

Throughout history, water has underpinned all Man's activities and helped him to survive and to realise his endeavours, but needs to be tamed and controlled and above all, used responsibly. Our water drinking habits, our disposal of waste, our agriculture, are but three examples where we have a large lasting impact on the environment in which the world lives, which cannot always be reversed.

I hope you enjoy reading this book, dipping into it, sharing its experiences by walking the walks; and at the same time join with me in a bid to prevent water waste and to promote a sustainable environment.

Jenny Stephenson.

GP, Sheffield. Summer 2019.

All photographs unless otherwise stated are the author's own.

All paintings and sketches are the author's own efforts.

All monies raised will go to Water Aid, Cavendish Cancer Care and other charities.

BEHIND THE TAP
We turn it on, but little do we think -
behind the tap, free flowing with clean freshness,
lies a history of technology, endeavour, grit and tears:
centuries of invention, striving
to bring us a safe cleanliness that we need.

ACKNOWLEDGEMENTS

I very much appreciate the tireless and valuable work of my Editor, Dr Diana Lightfoot. I am grateful to all the people I have met on the journey of researching and putting together this book, and to some family members and friends who kindly shot vital photos at my request. I am indebted to Mike Liversidge for his expert layout advice and printing.

I am also very grateful for the patience of everyone whenever I brought up the subject of toilets in polite company.

View of Agden Reservoir, Sheffield, from one of the footpaths around it. February 2019.

Chapter 1 - Wonderful Water

THE ESSENTIALS - WHAT, WHERE AND WHY

'A communal authority is best judged by the care it devotes to its water supply.' **(Aristotle)**

WHAT IS WATER?

Water is vital to life, as it forms part of every cell of every living thing and causes it to function.

The water molecule (H_2O) is made up of two hydrogen (H) atoms attached to one oxygen (O) atom. Water can be in three states, or types, of matter: liquid (water), gas (water vapour) and solid (ice). One cubic centimetre (cc) of water weighs one gram at 39.2°F (4°C), which is its maximum density. Water is unusual among hydrogen-containing substances in that it takes a lot of energy to boil or freeze.

If it was not so, fish and other animals living in water would die readily if there were to be climatic and temperature changes. All substances become less dense when they are heated and more dense when they are cooled. However, water as it cools to 4°C becomes more dense, then below this, it becomes less dense and turns into ice, able to float on water. The denser water will sink to the bottom of a pond, allowing fish and other living things to survive in it and not freeze.

WHERE IS WATER?

Most of the water in the world is in the seas, which cover 70% of the earth's surface. In total, 97% of the earth's water is salty, so only three percent is fresh water. Not all of this is accessible for drinking, as two-thirds of this is bound up as ice in Antarctica and the Arctic Polar ice caps. This leaves only one percent of the earth's water which is fresh and available for drinking.

THE WATER CYCLE

All our water is in fact recycled, ever since the world came into existence. Maybe, therefore, our own bath water will contain one or two molecules from that in which the Romans once bathed in their splendid Public Baths.

Energy from the sun drives the essential Water Cycle on which all living things rely, describing the movement of water above, below, and on the earth's surface.

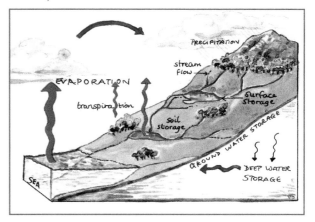

Water gathers in places on the earth's surface, in lakes, pools, rivers and seas, and with the sun's energy, the liquid water turns to vapour (evaporation) and rises to form clouds. When there is enough, it forms water droplets which then fall as rain, sleet or snow (precipitation), depending on temperature. This falls on the earth and can also run underground to rivers, lakes and even oceans there. Eventually this finds its way to the sea, where most evaporation of water takes place. The cycle repeats itself.

WHAT DO HUMANS NEED?

Water forms about 65% of an adult body, and 78% of a newborn baby's. Each day, therefore, a person needs to take in a certain amount of water to survive, but not too much. Men generally need about three litres of water a day, and women about half a litre less. This comes from what we drink and also what we eat. It is possible to drink more than recommended amounts, but this can sometimes cause a mineral imbalance. Children generally need about seven cups (1.75 litres) a day at 7 years of age, and ten to fourteen cups a day (up to 3.3 litres) by age 18.

Water allows blood to flow round our bodies; it dissolves minerals and foods, allowing digestion; it flushes waste out mainly by making urine; it regulates our body temperature by sweating and respiration; it forms a shock-absorber round the brain, spinal cord and unborn baby. It has many other uses at a cellular level.

WHAT DO PLANTS NEED?

Water transports nutrients into and through soil, so that they are available for plants to use. The best place to store water is in the soil or in the plants themselves. Soils with more clay or humus (organic matter) are best at holding water. Some plants are adapted for holding water in order to live in very dry environments such as the succulents like Houseleek (sempervivum – meaning 'always alive').

'Permaculture' refers to growing plants in such a way as to preserve the environment and conserve it for the future. The term was coined by Australian Bill Mollison in 1978, his concept based on sustaining natural systems. One example in a temperate climate may be the planting of a deciduous forest. This is the aim of some water companies, to exchange the pine trees for more sustainable deciduous forests on the slopes round reservoirs, containing trees like sycamore oak and ash. This will be discussed further in the final chapter.

WHY WATER?

All civilisations have, throughout history, been built around a water supply. Water is not only essential for life and living things, but for cities and dwellings.

The relationship of people to water through the centuries has been subject to ebb and flow. Until relatively recently, people have had a worry about their water – how to get it, is it clean, will it run out, for example, and they have felt very much at the mercy of the elements. In some communities this is still the case. It is a triumph of modern science and much hard work and planning, that today in the developed world water has become 'invisible', as it is obtained readily and of good quality, and has little impact on our lives.

This comes at great cost – financial and environmental. There are also big challenges ahead in terms of climate change, which could cause an increase in storms and sudden rainfall, yet periods of drought; and in terms of an increasing general world population (by about 80 million a year), increasing demand for clean water and disposal of waste.

If people and societies are more aware of what lies behind our taps, and what keeps our homes, streets and cities clean, then they may be more likely to revere and respect this miraculous commodity and use it carefully.

A further quote from Aristotle, who was an Ancient Greek philosopher, born in 384 BC:

'Special care should be taken of the health of the inhabitants, which will depend chiefly on the healthiness of the locality and of the quarter to which they are exposed, and secondly on the use of pure water; this latter point is by no means a secondary consideration. For the elements which we use the most and oftenest for the support of the body contribute most to health, and among these are water and air. Wherefore, in all wise states, if there is want of pure water, and the supply is not all equally good, the drinking water ought to be separated from that which is used for other purposes.'

Later in this book we shall see that he was right, and these vital facts were not taken into consideration even until relatively recently.

REFERENCES

https://www.usgs.gov/special-topic/water-science-school/science/water-you-water-and-human-body?qt-science_center_objects=0#qt-science_center_objects (Accessed 20.4.19)

http://nationalacademies.org/HMD/Activities/Nutrition/SummaryDRIs/DRI-Tables.aspx (Accessed 2.5.19)

https://chem.libretexts.org/ (Accessed 5.5.19)

Hoekstra, A.Y. Mekonnen, M.M. The Water Footprint of Humanity. PNAS February 28, 2012. ISBN: 109 (9) 3232-3237; https://doi.org/10.1073/pnas.

Sharp, Liz. Reconnecting People and Water – Public Engagement and Sustainable Urban Water management. Earthscan (Routledge) 2017. ISBN 978 0415 72845

Bell, G. The Permaculture Garden. Permanent Publications 2013. ISBN: 185 6230 279.

Chapter 2 - Wonderful Water
CONTENTS, CONTAMINATION AND QUALITY

TYPES AND USES OF WATER

Water can be thought of in terms of different 'types', meaning where they are found and their purpose. 'Blue' water refers to that in acquifers, lakes, rivers and reservoirs. 'Green' water means rain and the water in the soil. This type irrigates the crops, not 'blue' water. The Green water is not seen and makes up 74% of the total amount of water used by humans.

Of all water used by people, it has been estimated that 91% is used in agriculture, 5% for industrial use and 4% for domestic and city use. We consume far more water through the production of what we eat, especially in meat.

'Grey' water refers more to its purpose. It is defined as the amount of 'blue' water needed to dilute polluted water back to 'normal', but in everyday understanding, we take it to mean untreated or partly treated used water available to re-use.

'Black' water, however, refers to water and sewage from toilets.

SOME WATER CONTAMINANTS

Water by its very nature is found in many places on the earth's surface and beneath it, and as a result could be subject to contamination of many kinds. Our water treatment plants are aware of this and are equipped to de-contaminate our drinking water as discussed in the next chapter.

The Water Resources Act of 1991 is a UK Act of Parliament regulating water resources, water quality and pollution, and also flood defence.

MINERALS AND METALS: ALUMINIUM

Aluminium is found naturally in water, especially that draining from hills and moors, which is slightly acidic. This is increased in the presence of air pollution and 'acid rain'. Aluminium can be removed by coagulation and filtration; aluminium sulphate itself is used as a coagulant in water treatment processes.

There was a distressing disaster which occurred in Camelford, Cornwall in 1988. Accidental contamination of the drinking water supply with aluminium occurred when twenty tonnes of aluminium sulphate was inadvertently added to the wrong tank in the Water Treatment plant, leading to the drinking water outlet to the town. Aluminium was used to clarify the water, but several stages before it is sent out for drinking. Accordingly, the people received water with a high concentration of aluminium. The water authority had complaints after a short time interval, that some people were feeling unwell and that the water had a horrid taste. It took a couple of days for the mistake to be recognised, but two further weeks before people were informed of the error. It was however noted that 60,000 fish died in the nearby rivers following the flushing out process, and many people had definite symptoms. An investigation in 2005 concerning whether the symptoms were connected was initially inconclusive, but its Chair, Professor Frank Woods of Sheffield University, asked for further information. A final report in 2013 concluded that the incident had had no long-term health effects. Even now, uncertainties remain about this conclusion, which was reached due to lack of hard evidence at the time, and with a backdrop of a considerable political storm.

LEAD

In Victorian times, lead was used commonly in paint and water pipes, and lead poisoning, especially in children, was common. Toys were coated with lead paint, as were many other articles in the home and nursery, and the water pipes were made of lead. Young children are particularly at risk from lead, as it can affect their brain and nerve development as well as their general health.

Thankfully, the use of lead in homes was banned across Europe in 1970.

Water with high iron content

Lead can enter water from the corrosion of plumbing materials containing lead, especially if the water is soft and slightly acidic, as in some parts of Sheffield. Prior to 1970, homes were built with lead pipes and sometimes using lead solder to join pipes together. These mostly have now been replaced with plastic and copper piping. Rarely lead occurs naturally in groundwater, depending on the type of rock there, but lead levels in drinking water are checked regularly in the Water Treatment Centres, and they can be tested in homes on request. The current drinking water standard is no more than ten micrograms per litre.

BUGS AND BACTERIA: CAMPYLOBACTER

Campylobacter is a bacterium found in the intestines of many types of animals, domestic and wild, and is the most common bacterial cause of diarrhoeal illness. It is more often related to eating undercooked meat or contaminated food, for example if raw meat is allowed to come into contact with ready-to-eat cooked food. It can survive in water for some time but is destroyed by chlorine. The illness usually settles without antibiotics in people with normal immune systems. Other bacteria which can cause gastroenteritis include Salmonella and Escherichia coli, which are removed by water treatment processes and chlorination.

GIARDIA

Giardia, a protozoan (microscopic organism, this one with tails) is a leading but treatable cause of infectious gastroenteritis worldwide. In England, people contact these infections in the UK, not abroad. Infection mainly comes from water contaminated by giardia-containing faeces of infected people or animals, and there is an environmental health surveillance system in the UK and water supplies are tested regularly. The problem is that this parasite forms into cysts which are then resistant to chlorine, but mains water is also carefully filtered and disinfected in other ways. Washing hands after going to the toilet or before preparing food helps to prevent the spread, and people with it are treated with a course of an antibiotic.

CRYPTOSPORIDIUM

Cryptosporidium, another protozoan parasite, causes watery diarrhoea with abdominal pain, often with nausea and fever. It lasts much longer than most other types of gastroenteritis and may relapse once someone is apparently recovering. Antibiotics are ineffective.

Infection happens when a person ingests the cysts of this parasite from faecally-contaminated untreated water, from an infected person, or an infected animal or its dung. Those working with animals, or enjoying water sports or swimming, are at risk, as do those travelling to less developed countries, and children.

POLIO

Polio is a potentially devastating waterborne viral infection. It is a disease which can cause paralysis which may be permanent and life-threatening. Fortunately it is preventable by immunisation.

The first polio vaccine was developed by Jonas Salk and came into use in 1955. The oral polio vaccine came into general use in 1961 and was given to children on a sugar lump. It is now administered by injection, in combination with other vital vaccines.

OTHER ENTERIC ORGANISMS

There are several viruses which can cause gastroenteritis, and they come generally from the faeces of infected animals. There have been outbreaks related to private water

Covered spring at Edgemount Farm, Low Bradfield

supplies from surface water which has not been adequately treated. Open cisterns and reservoirs can be contaminated by birds, but after treatment, water for supply of houses is stored in covered reservoirs for this reason.

WEIL'S DISEASE

Also referred to as Leptospirosis, Weil's disease is caused by a corkscrew-shaped bacterium called Leptospira. It is spread by the urine of infected animals, mainly rats, mice and also pigs and cows. The disease can give a mild illness with headaches and muscle pains, or severe fever with meningitis and collapse.

Coming into contact with untreated fresh water like in a canal or lake containing the urine of infected animals, can cause the disease. Any person regularly canoeing, sailing or enjoying river swimming for example, should carry an alert in case they are taken ill suddenly. Shower as soon as possible after contact with the water and wear protective clothing if this contact is occupational.

Boats on Damflask reservoir

CHEMICAL CONTAMINATION HORMONES

It has been described in Lund University, Sweden, that the hormone ethinyl oestradiol found in contraceptive pills and Hormone Replacement Therapy can alter the genes of fish, changing their behaviour. The essential behaviour change is that they have difficulty catching their food and are less able to reproduce. Fish are especially susceptible to oestrogen effects, and this can cause entire populations to die out. The freshwater and sea fish studied were salmon, trout and roach.

This may have implications for human health, but amounts discovered are very small indeed. However, further research is being undertaken.

OTHER MEDICATIONS FOUND IN TAP WATER

A study in 2012 discovered that five commonly used medications had reached the treated tap water. Treated water was monitored in four UK sites over a year. The Drinking Water Inspectorate (set up in 1990 to provide independent examination of drinking water quality) checked these findings. They found traces of ibuprofen and naproxen (both anti-inflammatory drugs), carbamazepine (for epilepsy) and cocaine. The levels of these were found to be very low, and in the DWI's opinion, not expected to pose a risk to adult or child health over a lifetime. The recorded levels of these fell well short of those specified in the Water Resources Act.

The two ways in which these chemicals could reach the water supply is by a person who takes them regularly passing them out in their urine or faeces. The other way is when people flush unwanted medicines down the toilet, which is very much not recommended. Advice is to avoid over-stocking medicines and ask only for what is needed, and secondly any unused or out of date tablets be taken back to the Pharmacist.

Further to these findings, in 2018 York University researchers analysed waters in the rivers Foss and Ouse. They found 29 different types of pharmaceutical drug, but in tiny trace amounts, such as a millionth of a daily dose. Professor Boxall said: "There isn't any evidence for impact on human health from pharmaceuticals in rivers, but it definitely deserves more investigation." We await their findings.

WATER CONTAMINATION – CROPS AND CHEMICALS

Worldwide, contaminated water kills more people each year than wars and other types of violence put together. Ground water supplies drinking water for some people (via boreholes or springs); it is made up of rain which falls and sinks into the underground aquifers (storage areas of water) which can therefore be contaminated by polluted rain, pesticides, waste from landfill sites, industrial effluents and fertilisers. Surface water, from waterways, rivers reservoirs, can be contaminated by the same elements and from objects and substances which people throw into the water systems. These include phosphates from washing powders, detergents, and in the case of the sea – plastic and oil.

Drinking water needs to be protected from pesticides used to treat crops by spraying, or scattering (as in the case of slug pellets which contain metaldehyde). The farming industry is well aware of potential contamination and the implications for drinking water, and there have been many companies and campaigns which have been able to reduce such exposure. Farming practice has changed as a result, as has the production of pesticides. An arable farmer growing his crops now considers where the watercourses are on his land, and seeks to avoid the chemicals draining or falling into them. He will not apply the spray in wet weather or very dry weather, and will sometimes have to leave a margin of his field unused if it runs next to a river, especially if down a slope. This comes with it a cost in terms of reduced crop production, and requires time and planning.

Reproduced with permission of and thanks to the Crop Protection Association

The Common Agricultural Policy of the European Union was formed in 1962, with the objectives of providing affordable food for EU citizens and a fair standard of living for farmers. It promoted the mass production of crops and so pesticides became more important in order to maximise crop yields.

If we continue to produce food as we currently do, we can meet the demand for 40% more food by 2030, but this could create unsustainable pressures on water resources, energy, fossil fuels and it will increase our greenhouse gas emissions, (especially in the production of beef). Farmers are now looking to farm sustainably, using less water and fewer fertilisers and pesticides, with more efficient applications. Biotechnology will also provide improved seeds that can help increase crop production sustainably.

Around fields, landowners sometimes plant wild flowers in order to produce a habitat more attractive to pollinating insects. If used, herbicides are now carefully controlled in their chemical content and application. Not only does this have a widespread positive impact on wildlife, but the presence of beneficial insects on field margins provides additional pest control in neighbouring crops, reducing the need to apply insecticides later in the year. There has been some evidence that chemicals of the Neonicotinoid group may have had an impact on numbers of bees, but bee health has also been affected by habitat loss with building programmes, climate change and diseases like Varroa.

Pesticides are heavily regulated, but alternatives can be found in organic farming methods, which can be more costly with lower yields. Here, natural methods are relied upon to control pests and disease. These include well-designed crop rotations, encouraging natural predators, and developing good soil and crops which have some natural resistance to pests and diseases. There is some evidence that consuming organic foods with fewer pesticides may be related to a lowering in cancer risk, but this needs further testing. In any case, working towards preventing pesticides of whatever type entering the water supply is an important issue.

POLLUTION

Pollution of water can be from many sources. Acid rain is an important one. Rain or other type of precipitation becomes acid if sulphur dioxide and nitrogen oxide emissions react with atmospheric water molecules to produce sulphuric acid and nitric acid. These chemicals come from atmospheric pollution, chiefly from industries and the burning of fossil fuels. The results of this is costly to the environment and ecosystems, as it harms or kills trees and fish, amongst many other living things.

Other types of pollution of water are those from industrial waste discharged into rivers, which could contain anything from scrap metals, oil and chemicals, to concrete, sewage and teabags.

REFERENCES

https://www.epa.gov/ground-water-and-drinking-water/basic-information-about-lead-drinking-water. Accessed 8.5.19

http://dwi.defra.gov.uk/consumers/advice-leaflets/lead.pdf

Sharp, L. Reconnecting People and Water – Public Engagement and Sustainable Urban Water management. Earthscan (Routledge) 2017. ISBN 978 0415 72845

Mekonnen, M.M. and Hoekstra, A.Y. 2011. National Water Footprint Accounts: the Green, Blue and Grey Water Footprint of Production and Consumption, Vol 1, Main Report: UNESCO-IHE, Research Report Series No 50.

Minetti, C, Chalmers, R.M, Beeching, N, Probert, C, Lamsden, K. Giardiasis. BMJ 29 October 2016

Horne, S. Sibal, B. Sibal, N. Green, H.K. Cryptosporidium. British Journal of General Practice 2017; 67: 425-426. DOI: https://doi.org/10.3399/bjgp17X692501

Nikoleris, L. The estrogen receptor in fish and effects of synthetic estrogens in the environment - Ecological and evolutionary perspectives and societal awareness. 2016, Centre for Environmental and Climate Research (CEC) and Department of Biology, Faculty of Science, Lund University.128 pages.

Crop Protection Association, and Voluntary Initiative Community Interest Company publication 2017. 'Every Drop Counts' – advice on pesticides and water protection for farmers and sprayer operators.

https://pesticidesinperspective.org.uk/home accessed 19.1.19

https://www.soilassociation.org/organic-living/organic-farming/

Consumption of ultra-processed foods and cancer risk: results from NutriNet-Santé prospective cohort. BMJ 2018; 360 doi: https://doi.org/10.1136/bmj.k322 (Published 14 February 2018) BMJ 2018;360:k322

Hemler EC, Chavarro JE, Hu FB. Organic Foods for Cancer Prevention—Worth the Investment?. *JAMA Intern Med.* Published online October 22, 2018. doi:10.1001/jamainternmed.2018.4363

https://www.purewaterpeople.co.uk/blog/2014/09/drugs-in-water-supply/ accessed 10.5.19

http://dwi.defra.gov.uk/private-water-supply/installations/Micro-and-Chem.pdf accessed 10.5.19

https://www.legislation.gov.uk/ukpga/1991/57/contents Water Resources Act 1991.

https://www.york.ac.uk/news-and-events/news/2018/research/prescription-drugs-contaminate-york-rivers/

Environment Agency. 'Waterwise on the Farm'.

Version 2. March 2007.

Chapter 3 - Wonderful Water

WATER TREATMENT

A Water Treatment Works (WTW) turns 'raw' water in a reservoir or river into water with a quality fit for drinking. Raw water from these sources is open directly to the environment, so multiple treatment steps are required to clean it up.

Wastewater, by contrast, is made up from water used in the home or industries, and from rain from roofs and from the streets. It is guided down drains and enters sewers which run under the roads along to the Sewage Works. It will be discussed further in Section 4.

FROM LAKES TO LIPS – TREATING WATER TO MAKE IT DRINKABLE

Water companies generally have their own Education Centres, where schoolchildren and anyone else can enjoy a day of instructional and most interesting activities relating to water. The message of understanding and appreciating this valuable resource starts at a young age. Yorkshire Water and Severn Trent are no exceptions, and I was able to spend a morning with Yorkshire Water at the Ewden Treatment Works.

Ewden Treatment Works supplies 45 million litres of treated water to Sheffield. The process flows through many stages as below.

The water treatment plants are usually installed near a reservoir. More Hall reservoir near Stocksbridge, South Yorkshire, is a Compensation reservoir which flows into the River Don when needed to adjust its level via Ewden Beck. The nearby Broomhead reservoir is of Supply type and yields its water through a wide grill or screen to remove leaves, twigs and other things from the outdoors into a large pipe. The water is conducted to the WTW turning a turbine which produces a third of the power used on site. It also goes through a pre-treatment process of Magnetic Ionic Exchange. Water passes through a resin under an electromagnet, which reduces turbidity and the amount of coagulant needed to clarify the water. The resin can be reconditioned and reused, reducing cost.

The first treatments for the raw water are **Coagulation** and **Flocculation.** These are the processes whereby particles in the water causing it to look muddy are joined together in order to make larger particles, which are easier to separate from the water. This will remove clay and mud, algae, protozoa, bacteria and viruses. This is achieved using magnetised iron resin, and the result is a scummy sludge. This is made to float on the surface by bubbling air through the water.

The next process is **Clarification** when this sludge is removed by a scraper as the water passes over a small waterfall. The clarified water passes on to **Filtration**.

The filters are made of gravel and sand, through which the water passes. This process removes he last traces of the sludge.

At Ewden where only reservoir water is treated, trace metals such as Manganese, Iron and Aluminium are removed on second stage filters, and sodium hypochlorite (bleach) is added between the two sets of filters. This acts as an oxidising agent bringing the metals out of solution as oxides.

The water is tested chemically throughout.

Disinfection uses sodium hypochlorite (dilute bleach), which is produced on site by the electrolysis of sodium chloride (salt) solution. It kills the pathogenic (disease-causing) bacteria and is put in dose-wise after the filtering process.

Ozone is used to remove further germs. Following that, metals like Manganese which may be present, are removed by granular activated carbon. Further **Chlorination** takes place as a final step before the treated water leaves the Works and enters the Yorkshire Water Mains Pipe Network, its total length being about 20,000 miles. This forms a Grid for distribution to homes.

WE'RE PART OF IT

We not only benefit from this clean, assured supply of water, but we are part of its success. For us, it is 'sorted' by the water professionals – with our help. Our part to play happens every single day: taking what we need, then turning off the tap; re-using where we can; reducing our consumption when there is relative shortage of this essential commodity.

How can Water Companies engage the people who benefit from their product? In the early years, people were fully engaged because they physically had to collect the water for their families and bring it home. They were open to disease from untreated and contaminated water. Moving through the centuries, water became a symbol of civilisation and development, with larger cities being built next to major rivers and water supplies.

From Victorian times, the public was encouraged to rely solely on Water Companies to provide a seamless solution in their homes and places of work; they did not need to worry about it, any of them. Powerful symbols of Progress stood like fortresses – Victorian boiler houses and pumps; magnificent sewerage systems, new reservoirs and dams.

Then, in the 1980's people began to realise that environmental issues were important, and that the public was part of it. Few knew where their own sewer ran, for example, until it caused problems for them. The Water Companies began to draw people into knowledge about water, and with this, some responsibility for its careful use. Back in 1993, for example, the Rivelin WTW opened its doors to the public to look round at the process, and it was well attended.

Perhaps our use of water is sustainable if the public are more engaged. We all are aware of climatic changes – periods of drought and times of torrential rain. A fresh approach is needed, based on increasing public interest in water.

CHLORINATION OF WATER

Dr Alexander Cruikshank Houston was born in 1865 and graduated in 1892 from Edinburgh Medical School. He studied public health and waterborne disease such as cholera, of great importance at the time. He developed water analysis skills starting with moorland bogs, and then moved on to examining waste and drinking water standards in London. His next job was to investigate the stinking mass of effluent from water engineer Bazalgette's pipes at Crossness and Barking sewage beds in order to find out what bacteria they contained. This was new material, never before studied. He concluded that anti-bacterial methods of water treatment were safer and better than chemical treatment processes. He also set the standards of what could be considered safe drinking water.

His skills were called upon to help when Lincoln developed a typhoid crisis in 1905. He recommended the use of 'hypochlorite of soda' to sterilise the drinking water, as it released chlorine which denatures protein by oxidising it, thereby killing living things made of protein, including bacteria.

Chlorine was actually discovered in the eighteenth century by a Swedish chemist Carl Wilhelm Scheele while investigating something else. A product called 'cream of lime' came to be used to bleach materials such as linen. Chlorine became known for its cleansing properties in 1834, when a Bristol-based Dr Lansdown found that it treated cholera, while using a mixture containing it for treating diarrhoea.

The Public then had to be won over, as chlorination of the general drinking water supplies took place. In Lincoln, there were no new cases of cholera once the water had been chlorinated, yet people grumbled at its taste especially when made into tea! They were taking cleansed, safe, cholera-free water for granted, finding objection to peripheral issues.

For London, Dr Houston developed a method of regular water testing and reporting. He also discovered by careful research that letting water stand, for example in a reservoir, also helped to rid it of some bacteria. He even drank a sample of the stored water himself, which had previously contained the cholera germ, and was unharmed.

The actual chlorination of London's water commenced during World War 1, in 1916, expedited as it was by wartime needs. The word 'chlorine' was omitted in the newspapers of the time, due possibly to its wartime associations in the public mind with chlorine gas. There was however some negative public opinion regarding 'chemicals' in the water but people came to realise that it was safer for themselves and their children, and the matter became taken for granted.

FLUORIDATION OF WATER

One of the most important ideas of the new National Health Service in 1948 was that of preventing disease rather than solely treating it. At about this time, post WW2, there was a great rebuilding of the UK, especially around London which had suffered extensive bombing damage. Drinking water became a focal point in this debate of prevention and social equality, fluoridation being one of the main issues, causing some controversy and public dissent.

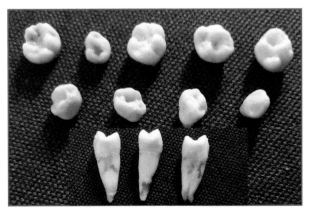

Primary dentition (baby teeth), some with (brown) decay, and three wisdom teeth

The story of fluoridation began with a mystery staining of the teeth first described by dentist Frederick McKay in Colorado in 1912. From those observations, he realised that it may be related to the water supply, but also concluded that this staining seemed to protect against dental caries.

In the UK, a dentist Mr. Norman Ainsworth had found dental staining similar to McKay's description of "Rocky Mountain Mottled Teeth". As part of a study for the Medical Research Council in 1925, Ainsworth examined over 4,000 children and, for the first time, proved that those living in areas where mottled teeth were commonest tended to have much less dental decay than those with less mottling of their teeth.

Fluoride levels vary in soil and therefore water; in the UK highest levels are found in Norwich, Cambridge, Cheshire, Tyneside, whereas others are relatively low like in Sheffield. Waters with high levels of fluoride content are mostly found at the foot of mountains and in areas where the sea has made geological deposits. Lower levels are found where the water supply is from rivers and moorland.

During the Second World War, children from South Shields, an industrial town on the River Tyne, were evacuated to the Lake District. The Senior School Dentist for Westmoreland noted that the evacuees had far better teeth than local children. Robert Weaver, a dentist working for the Ministry for Education, was aware of the work being carried out in America and had the fluorine content of South Shields water analysed. It proved to be around 1.4ppm, much higher than is present in most water supplies. He had North Shields' (on the other bank of the Tyne) water analysed; this proved to have a fluoride content of only 0.25ppm. In 1944 Weaver examined 1,000 children on either side of the Tyne. This study demonstrated much lower decay rates in both permanent and deciduous teeth in South Shields. This study was the first to describe the effects on the primary dentition of fluoride content of the water.

Water naturally fluoridated at 1ppm clearly benefitted dental health. This was subjected to further study in 1955, which also reported reductions in decay of about 50% or more if fluoride was added to drinking water in a few urban areas in the USA. That was at a time

Fluoride-containing toothpaste selection

Fluoride-containing mouthwash selection

when fluoridated water offered the only significant source of fluoride.

The introduction of fluoridated toothpaste in the early 1970s has provided an important source of fluoride and this is thought to have contributed to the fall in decay rates experienced the world over. However, dental decay is still more common in areas of least water fluoride content.

This shows that following an astute observation, a public health opportunity is found, then subjected to rigorous testing, and put into practice if there are no ill effects.

One potential problem with adding fluoride is Fluorosis, a harmless mottling or staining of the teeth enamel, but in very high-level intake, fluoride could also affect the bones. According to WHO this would be a rare occurrence not resulting from supplemented water alone. However, a large study in 2011, and several others, have shown no link of fluoride at recommended levels with the bone tumour osteosarcoma, and another in 2014 showed no link with damage to nerves. The York Report 2000 concluded that the 'fluoridation of water is a cost-effective public health strategy for reducing tooth decay in a population. Fluoride has been found to be highly protective against dental caries, and there is no convincing evidence of any adverse risk to human health by the introduction of water fluoridation.'

Removal of excessive fluoride from drinking-water is difficult and expensive: the preferred option is to find a supply of safe drinking-water with safe fluoride levels. The WHO guideline value for fluoride in water is 1.5 mg/litre of water (or 1.5 parts per million, ppm).

The controversial backlash commenced in 1953, initiated by the British Housewives League as trials of fluoridation were about to start in several areas of the UK. At the time, fear was partly allayed by the assurance that fluoride is a naturally occurring substance found in water anyway, and some areas lacked the required amount.

In 1960 the anti-fluoridation movement consolidated under the National Pure Water Association and the objections centred more on the feeling that people were being 'medicated' without their consent, their liberties being infringed. In 1963 the Ministry for Health issued approval for all local health authorities to instruct the water companies to start adding fluoride in areas which had low drinking water levels. People felt this was being forced upon them, fuelled by lobbies elsewhere, and publication of questioning books like *Silent Spring* (Rachel Carson) with its concerns over environmental toxicology. The central move therefore did not go ahead and this was announced in 1968, but Birmingham was one of the first towns to have taken up fluoridation in 1964. The Water Act of 2003 states that a health authority can direct a water company to fluoridate the water supply in an area, if it is required and technically feasible. The authority must consult with the local community and businesses in the relevant area.

In 2019, about 10% of the UK population (that is, just over 6.1 million people) live in areas of adequate fluoride supply, either naturally or added. It compares with 70% of the USA population drinking fluoridated water. Sheffield's water contains only 0.1ppm of fluoride and there are high rates of dental decay in adults as well as children. This continues, and in 2007 the decision was reluctantly taken not to supplement the Sheffield water with this natural substance, and the matter is to be reviewed, taking in all the reliable evidence available.

The Water Fluoridation: Health monitoring report for England 2018 concludes that 'water fluoridation is an effective and safe public health measure to reduce the frequency and severity of dental decay, and narrow the differences in dental health between more and less deprived children and young people.' Sheffield's Oral Health Improvement Strategy 2018-2021 has an oral health vision that 'all Sheffield residents should be able to speak, smile and eat with confidence and without pain or discomfort from their teeth or mouths'. This can be addressed through improving overall oral health, concentrating Public Health measures in areas where children and young people experience the most dental decay.

The scientific evidence needs to be carefully assessed before basing decisions upon it, as there are many examples of mis-quoting. It is an emotive issue that flows deeper than the concerns of fluoride itself, touching on the freedom to choose.

KANT AND THE PHILOSOPHY OF AUTONOMY

It is a basic human right for a person to be able to make their own decisions, using the information available. This is what is meant by Autonomy.

The philosophy of autonomy is attributed to Immanuel Kant (1724-1804), a German philosopher, who saw personal autonomy as the capacity to decide for oneself and pursue a course of action in one's life.

These ideas can be applied to the situations where people resist central decision-making by those in authority, as there is an innate distrust that the interests of the individual are not being taken into account. Such resistance has been witnessed in scenarios such as vaccination as well as chlorination of water. As citizens we need to have information of such a quality and reliability that we can assess fully the pros and cons, how they apply to us and also to the community in which we live. Does the benefit to us and to the community outweigh the possible drawbacks?

Public engagement therefore needs to be thorough and automatic whenever any action is considered which has an effect on the community. People can only make a balanced decision if they have true reliable information in a way they can understand and use.

REFERENCES

I am most grateful to Debbie Hanson, Health Improvement Principal, Public Health Sheffield, for assistance with references and information.

https://www.bma.org.uk/-/media/files/pdfs/.../bma_fluoride.pdf accessed 7.3.19.
NHS CRD (2000) A Systematic Review of Public Water Fluoridation (CRD Report No.18), York, UK, NHS Centre for Review and Dissemination, University of York. [Available at http://www.york.ac.uk/inst/crd/fluorid.htm]
BMJ 2000; 321 doi: https://doi.org/10.1136/bmj.321.7265.855 (Published 07 October 2000) Cite this as: BMJ 2000;321:855
https://www.dentalhealth.org/water-fluoridation-policy (accessed 7.3.19)
https://www.change.org/p/bedford-borough-council-stop-water-fluoridation-in-bedford-borough
https://www.pontefractandcastlefordexpress.co.uk/news/health/should-fluoride-be-added-to-our-tap-water-wakefield-council-to-hear-the-evidence-1-7691748
Gelinas, Juliana. The Lancet Updates: Neurology. Vol 13 issue 7. Pages 647-648. July 01 2104
Dr Gregg Fell, Sheffield's Public Health Report, 2018 – http://www.sheffield.gov.uk/home/public-health/director-public-health.html
Water Fluoridation: Health monitoring report for England 2018. Public Health England. Published March 2018 PHE publications PHE supports the UN gateway number: 2017777
It concludes-
The findings of this report agree with the view that water fluoridation is an effective and safe public health measure to reduce the frequency and severity of dental decay, and narrow differences in dental health between more and less deprived children and young people.
Water Fluoridation and Human Health in Australia: Questions and Answers -
National Health and Medical Research Council NHMRC Public Statement 2017: Water fluoridation and human health in Australia.
http://www.waterjournal.co.uk/features/processes/coagulation-and-flocculation-improvement-through-understanding/
http://dwi.defra.gov.uk/private-water-supply/installations/Treatment-processes.pdf
https://www.youtube.com/watch?v=9z14l51ISwg
https://www.yorkshirewater.com/sites/default/files/How%20to%20make%20water%20safe%20to%20drink.pdf

Chapter 1 - Cities and Civilisations.

REMARKABLE ROMANS

The Roman Empire started with the Founding of Rome in the 8th Century BC, and ended with its collapse in the 5th Century AD. It expanded to become one of the largest empires in the ancient world, though still ruled from one city, covering roughly 20% of the world population at the time.

A long Roman aqueduct found between Pisa and Lucca, Italy

The influence of the Romans was substantial, not only in terms of its span of thirteen centuries, but its sophisticated civilisation and culture. The remarkable Romans brought us Government, roads, cities, industries to name a few, as well as the roots of many languages. However, the Roman systems of water usage formed the basis of many of the assets established throughout their Empire.

Aqueduct, Perugia, Italy. Now a footpath.

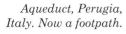

A shallow pool or Impluvium, for rainwater collection in the entrance of a villa.

THE ROMAN TOWN

Roman towns were built to the same plan. The layout was in the form of a grid, with streets at right angles to each other and parallel to the main roads. There were villas, houses and even blocks of flats. In the centre there were temples and a large square called the Forum. It was used as a market-place as well as a space for meetings, government, worship and debate. There were shops and offices surrounding it.

The Romans developed a system of capturing water and using it in their towns, separating and removing waste in an underground sewer.

It wasn't an open festering disease-ridden sump or stream as in later times in England but a clean wastewater system like today's.

Aqueducts or bridges brought a supply of nearby clean water into the town. The Romans discovered that lead could be easily melted and used to make pipes to conduct this water into the public drinking

fountains in the streets, as in this one in Pompeii. Only the rich people had their own home water supply with a branching-off lead pipe as seen in the photo in Pompeii. The public toilets were situated in most main

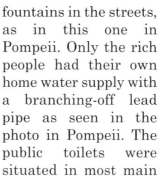

streets, emptying into the sewers underground, and again the rich would have their own toilet. The one on the previous page is easily missed in one of the posh villas in Pompeii but I spotted it.

The Romans are perhaps more famous for their Public Baths. These were generally built in a complex which also gave access to restaurants, games rooms and even libraries sometimes. The Baths were a place of social gathering as well as washing and refreshment. They were very popular; there were a total of 170 such Baths in Rome during the reign of Augustus.

The Baths had their own constant supply of fresh water. The large one in the city of Bath was fed by a spring; others had piped water but both were heated inside the complex by a Hypocaust system. This involved a furnace heating the air space under the floor and in the walls, which also allowed this hot air to be circulated under and around the baths themselves.

There was a set of Baths for women and a separate one for men. Each was divided into three rooms. The first was the Tepidarium which was warm – the air and water temperature were at about our room heat. This was the first bath which people entered after taking off their clothes. Next came the Caldarium which was hot. It made the people sweat. After laying about in this for a while, the person's slave came and administered a massage with scented oil which was then scraped off with a type of palette knife, or Strigil. Following that procedure, the person would take the plunge into the Frigidarium - the cold bath. This experience was meant to invigorate them and leave them feeling refreshed.

So, for reasons of cleanliness, health and socialising, the Baths were one of the central resources of the Roman town.

The main Roman bath in Bath, Avon.

This photograph reveals another aspect to the Romans' appreciation of bathing in water – that of the spiritual dimension. I found this illustration of a man diving into the water of the Unknown on a tomb dated about 480 BC in Paestum, Italy.

The inflow of clean water into a Roman city was therefore plentiful enough to cater for bathing, cleaning, eating and drinking. It flowed into a city like Pompeii in large underground cavernous corridors, as pictured.

Chapter 2 - Cities and Civilisations.
EARLY SHEFFIELD HISTORY

HILLS AND WELLS – IN THE BEGINNING

Sheffield (Escafeld) was a settlement at the confluence of the rivers Sheaf and Don at the time of the Norman Conquest. The rivers met at the 'Sheaf Field' at which a castle was built and the settlement's first bridge crossing, between seven hills, the River Don and seven of its tributaries. Geologically Sheffield stood at the junction of the mill-stone grit (porous sandstone) with the coal seams. On top of the sandstone bed there was a thick layer of clay and under all of this was a rich supply of water. Boreholes could easily reach this and there were plenty of springs too. This allowed early inhabitants to extract clean water from natural wells, rivers and small storage pools. Sheffield grew to become a market town in the 14th century with its feudal three-field system for crops and common grazing land. The rivers were an important source of fish. By the start of the 16th century the town was producing cutlery, mainly for sale out of Sheffield, the industry and grinding being made possible by the fast-flowing rivers.

The high moorlands around Sheffield provided water flows through the fertile valleys and the town itself was always known to be hilly. The north side was thickly wooded. The industrial part of the town was central, where the two rivers met; towards Rotherham there was higher ground with many streams which was the park of the Earls of Shrewsbury, used for hunting. To start with, communal wells existed in the High Street of the early town and the children were sent to collect water in buckets balanced on their heads. Even then there were regulations to ensure cleanliness of water, such as those forbidding the washing of meat in water used for drinking.

BARKER'S POOL

In the seventeenth century many public wells were sunk and maintained by the Town Trustees. The first completely artificial reservoir for public use was the work of a Mr Barker, who built a pool on the City Hall site. The exact date of construction is unclear, but it had walls and was fed by nearby wells. Local people accessed its water using buckets and barrels. It had one water outlet leading into an open gulley, not a pipe. This gulley led all the way down the middle of Fargate and then the High Street as an open stream. Water was released periodically into this gulley to allow shopkeepers to clean the fronts of their premises after a day's work and it also was an important reserve if fire broke out. However, it is unclear if this supply of water became contaminated and helped to spread disease, but it was closed in 1793 and the gulley was piped.

In 1737 several small reservoirs called the Whitehouse Dams were constructed privately by the River Don in Hillsborough. They were connected with other small reservoirs built in Crookes Valley in about 1785. The supply was piped to a distributing dam at Portobello and from there to a small cistern at Division Street.

PROBLEMS OF POPULATION

By the turn of the nineteenth century, Sheffield had become densely populated, people being drawn into the town in order to work in the industries there. Houses were built fairly quickly and densely, and often for the poorer people, back to back.

However, as the population increased, so did their waste and cesspools were dug into the thick clay to collect this. It drained away only very slowly, resulting in the previously fresh water becoming contaminated with the waste of all kinds. People became ill and there were high death rates in children and adults due to the contaminated drinking water. A person was expected to live only to the age of 30 or 40 years in the early 1800's. The life expectancy in 2018 was double that in 1840.

Sheffield was becoming strangled by its own effluent. Something had to change. The link between dirt and disease had to be recognised. This was slow to happen, as it was in other parts of England, notably London. The Sheffield cholera outbreak of 1832 began to focus attention on the cause of disease but even when the link with dirty water was discovered the authorities were reluctant to act.

The following chapters will cover the convoluted story of the scientific discoveries and the socio-political changes which had to happen in order to bring about change – essential change to protect peoples' lives. Clean drinkable water and the removal of waste were fundamental in all this.

In order to effect change someone had to be in charge and take stock of the mounting problems. Water was one of the work streams of the Sheffield Town Trust.

SHEFFIELD TOWN TRUST

The Sheffield Town Trust dates back to 1297 and for the greater part of the succeeding six centuries it was responsible for many of the duties now undertaken by the Local Authority or City Council. It is one of the oldest charities in England.

The Records of the Burgery (Town Council) dated 1897 reveals that Sheffield Town Trustees, following the Decree of Commissioners in 1681, had a public duty to use their funds in order to improve life for the citizens of Sheffield. (Their funds came primarily from rents collected from the freeholders of the town). Among their many roles, as listed in the Record, they were instrumental in overseeing the water supplies to Sheffield in those early days, cleaning and caring for the public wells. They set up a working group to repair the Lady Bridge and Barker Pool in 1666, as well as general repairs to roads, and also charitable deeds.

In 1722 they promoted a scheme for improving navigation of the River Don (Dun as it was known then) and this supported local industry. They commissioned bore holes to be dug in order to search for new, clean supplies as the town grew larger (1755). Prior to that, the Town Trustees had organised engineers and funds to build some of the first reservoirs (near the White House in 1713 and in Crookes Valley in 1737).

In 1831 the Trustees collected funds and set up a group including local doctors, to plan how to cope with a cholera outbreak, should there be one. Their plans had to come into effect in 1832, when the outbreak did strike Sheffield, the most notable victim being John Blake, the Master Cutler.

The Sheffield Cholera Monument

At the beginning of the nineteenth century, the Town Trustees built a new Town Hall which later became the Court House (now the Old Town Hall). The current Town Hall was opened by Queen Victoria in 1897.

The Sheffield Improvement Act (1818) led to the appointment of commissioners who gradually took over the responsibility for the policing and cleansing of the town and for its water supply from the Town Trust. In 1843, when Sheffield was incorporated as a borough, these responsibilities passed to the newly elected town council led by the town's Mayor (it became a city with a Lord Mayor in 1893). The Town Trust therefore became wholly a charity with funds to support worthy causes and survives today as a land and property owner and active charity.

'THE SANATORY CONDITION OF THE BOROUGH OF SHEFFIELD' – 1847

A report about the 'Sanatory Condition' of Sheffield was written in 1847 by Professional Chemist, James Haywood and William Lee, Civil Engineer. They had been commissioned by the new Sheffield Town Council to investigate the water supply and drainage systems in the town. It was known at the time that there were many health problems and deaths which were associated with what the Victorians referred to as 'filth'.

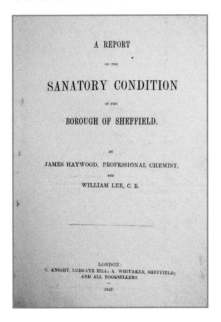

'The Sanatory Condition of the Borough of Sheffield' 1847

Mr Haywood described the work as 'a laborious task' which they brought to a close 'after considerable difficulty'. His story was not a happy one.

The first forty-six pages were devoted to a distressing list of dwellings in the centre of Sheffield which were drowning in their own refuse and midden, and as a result had a high rate of child deaths and diseases. He described the 'night soil', meaning the effluent from toilets (or 'privies') flowing out into the streets. It leaked into cellars of other houses, became mixed with carcasses of dead animals from the local abattoirs, seeped up the walls, formed stagnant hazardous cesspools around the houses where children played and people tried to work. It was truly appalling. The stench was indescribable. At the time, people thought that the smell of bad air or 'miasma', was the cause of disease, and no wonder.

The investigators' descriptions would make a person cry. We read that 'the drainage from this pestiferous heap into adjoining houses is abominable'; 'a privy of the most loathsome description'; 'pallid faces peering out of the darkness, wracked with fever and disease'… ..the list goes on. Houses were built back-to-back, and in some cases a double privy would be used by up to 21 families. Even the rivers were full of rubbish and excrement, the weirs forming giant pools of disease-causing morass. He recorded that people suffered from 'fever' most of the time; typhus (transmitted by lice), consumption (TB), Scarlet Fever, pneumonia and at one time even malaria.

There was no cleansing service of any kind in those days. There was no removal of refuse, no clearing of the cesspools and no treatment of the toilets. All the filth accumulated, stifling and killing the people who had no choice but to live within it. The report continued with an investigation into dangerous heating systems and ventilation in public buildings and factories, recommendations for street cleaning and using midden waste as fertiliser for farm fields.

The conclusions of these eminent gentlemen were that 'some immediate measures are certainly required here to preserve the lives of the inhabitants'. A centrally run cleansing service was required urgently. The dirty slums needed clearing and new housing built, with cleaner sanitary arrangements including 'water closets' to replace the 'disgusting privies' and drainage systems installed throughout. They recommended the construction of brick sewers and emphasised the need for an increased clean water supply. Sheffield was probably not alone in these problems, which were faced by all industrial towns of the time.

This report had a great impact. It described the desire to reduce the 'enormous amount of preventable pauperism and misery' by using the Poor Law (of 1834) to better effect. We saw that the first reservoirs began to be built soon after, and Sheffield's sewer and drainage system was built later by the Town Council in the 1870s. Further major works were carried out on this in 1910 as the population expanded further. At first raw sewage was pumped into rivers, but in 1886 a sewage treatment plant was constructed in Blackburn Meadows, at the eastern end of the city. It is sited there today, larger and more sophisticated, near Meadowhall.

REFERENCES

Acknowledgement and grateful thanks to Dr Julie MacDonald for historical advice about Sheffield Town Trust.

J Haywood, W Lee. 'Report on the Sanatory Condition of the Borough of Sheffield.' 1847. London: C Knight, Ludgate Hill; A Whittaker, Sheffield and All Booksellers. Courtesy of Sheffield Archives.

Edward Vickers. A Popular History of Sheffield. Applebaum Bookshop Publishing Ltd Sheffield. Revised 1987 ISBN 0-906787-04-1)

Leader, John Daniel. The Records of the Burgery of Sheffield, commonly called The Town Trust. 1897. The Sheffield Independent Press Limited, Fargate, Sheffield.

© Sheffield Libraries Archives and Information 2006 With thanks to Martin Olive, former Local Studies Librarian, who originally compiled this history.

Sources for the Study of Cholera in Sheffield © Sheffield Libraries Archives and Information 2009.

Sheffield libraries archives and information archives and local studies: A Short History of Sheffield

https://www.sheffield.gov.uk/content/dam/sheffield/docs/libraries-and-archives/archives-and-local-studies/research/Short-History--PDF--428-KB-.pdf Accessed 19.2.19.

Professor Binfield, Clyde, OBE. Origins of the Sheffield Town Trust -

http://www.sheffieldtowntrust.org.uk/history.htm Accessed 21.2.19

Chapter 3 - Cities and Civilisations.

SOURCING OUR WATER

WATER DOWSING

Water dowsing, (rather than 'divining' which is a sort of divination) has for millennia been used to locate water resources underground, water being essential for life and civilisation. Water dowsing first appeared in Chinese inscriptions from about 2500BC although there is no evidence that it was used by the Romans. Specialist Dowsers also can detect other underground resources. They have been employed to locate pipes, metals and gems, minerals, archaeological artefacts, and even unexploded bombs and enemy tunnels in the Vietnam War in the 1960's.

Water dowsing isn't exactly 'scientific' and for it there is no logical proof, but it does have credibility as it attempts to scrutinise parts of the earth unseen and discern the source of a vital commodity. There is no reason why it should work. I wonder if the person is sufficiently experienced to know from topography where aquifers may be running, taking clues from what they are seeing, hearing, and smelling. Bore hole drilling often employs a water dowser to advise where to dig the bore hole. Perhaps they feel it in the body rather than use the wand or stick. There is no denying, however, that it can work.

Dowsers use a freshly cut 'wand' or forked twig of wood which oscillates when in the vicinity of water. Otherwise, pairs of L-shaped metal rods may cross to mark the spot, or a pendulum may swing. Holding the chosen instrument lightly, the dowser walks slowly over the search area, focussing the mind on the water being sought, and remaining intently alert to any twitches that indicate a required change in direction, or signal successful detection.

An unusual method of finding water was recounted in The Times newspaper of 12th February 2018. A 16-month old cocker spaniel, trained by ex-military personnel, could sniff out leaks of water in rural areas. The spaniel can detect one particle of an odour in a billion so he can smell out chlorine, which makes up one part per million of tap water. He was taught to sit down and stare at the source once found and was rewarded with a tennis ball or a biscuit. He was put to work for United Utilities in the Northwest of England which records an annual average of 27,000 leaks of domestic water supply.

FROM WHERE DOES SHEFFIELD'S WATER COME?

Up until the early nineteenth century people gathered their water for themselves. In 1830 the Sheffield Water Company (SWC) started to create an organised piped water supply as well as digging the first two reservoirs (Redmires and Hadfield). At the time the population of Sheffield was 90,000.

Then Sheffield was struck by a disaster which forced the authorities to think again about how water supplies were cared for and planned. Dale Dyke Dam burst its banks in 1864. This eventually led to the relinquishing of the Company's responsibilities.

In 1887, Sheffield Corporation took over the water supply for the then 320,000 population. A Water Undertaking means an undertaking for the supply of water for public consumption, and is a term embracing the legal requirement of the Water Company to provide water to the inhabitants. In 1887 there were 68,000 houses, about 1 in 30 having a fixed bath, and 1 in 17 a water closet type of toilet. Two public swimming baths had been built by then and 270 miles of water mains laid.

In 1897 the Little Don Valley works were constructed with Langsett impounding reservoir and Underbank compensation reservoir, and sand filter beds. Water was getting cleaner as the link between ill health and dirty water became obvious. Collaboration of Water Companies occurred in 1899, Sheffield making a partnership with Derby Leicester and Nottingham for constructing further reservoirs in the Derwent Valley – see Section 6, Chapter 1.

As the population grew ever steadily larger more reservoirs were needed for Sheffield and other districts. In 1913 work was started on the Ewden Valley with Broomhead and More Hall reservoirs, and a filtering station. This was followed in 1919 by the River Don pumping works for the filtering and re-use of river water, intended to maintain the supply of drinking water in times of drought.

The distribution of supplies was originally based on a simple gravitational system, the water being conveyed by mains piping from supply reservoirs in the West to service reservoirs within the City from which service mains conveyed water to the peoples' homes. There is a considerable difference in altitude over our hilly city so it was necessary as development took place, to install pumps at strategic points in order to boost supply to higher places. More pumping stations were therefore built. Service reservoirs and water towers provided storage near the point of use to balance the steady flow from the source against the uneven demand.

In the 1960's water had to be sought far outside Sheffield district in order to satisfy the needs of the increasing population. It came via an aqueduct from the river Derwent in North Yorkshire. It required new pipes and pumping stations, and much expenditure.

This 1968 Water Undertaking was compiled by ten water boards and associations. The report details the water supplies to 237 square miles of Sheffield covering 739,789 persons in Sheffield and 250,259 in the periphery. The total supply for all purposes was 64.7 million gallons per day which worked out as 30 gallons per head per day (136 litres). The capital expenditure for the year 1968 was £ 20, 481.

In 1974 the Yorkshire Water Authority (YWA) took over all the water boards and the Local Authority undertakings of Yorkshire. Its offices were in the Castle Market building in Sheffield. At that time the average household use was 50 gallons a day and Sheffield was supplied with nearly 57 million gallons each day for households and industries. In addition, over 16 million gallons were used for compensation water for rivers.

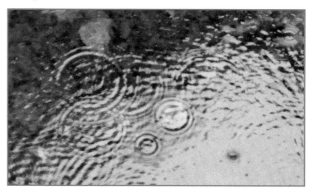

New water treatment works were commissioned in 1985 at Langsett which supplied Sheffield, Barnsley and Rotherham, It complied with the latest EEC standards for drinking water. Extension to Redmires Water Treatment works was completed in 1988 using the then new 'Sirofloc' process followed by pressure filtration. See section 6, chapter 1.

YWA became a private company (YWA plc) in 1989. By 1991 the domestic consumption of water had become 28 gallons (128 litres) per person per day.

Sheffield's water is now supplied by Yorkshire Water and it comes from the river Derwent and the river Ouse in North Yorkshire, rather than from the reservoirs on the moorland around Sheffield. Severn Trent company, on the other hand, uses this water along with other reservoirs, to serve a wide area from the Bristol Channel to the Humber. It covers East Midlands and Shropshire, and the area includes Rotherham and Derbyshire.

River water is classed as 'hard' as it contains more minerals from the rocks over which it flows. Water from reservoirs tends to be 'soft' as it drains from the moorlands around the reservoirs. The water companies have underground pipe networks through which water can be moved or sourced, so where we get our water will change from time to time, depending on general water levels. People tend to use more water in the dry summer months so alternative sources are needed such as boreholes or rivers, or getting water from other areas in the UK, in order to maintain supplies.

It is a complex process which goes on without our noticing it. We are part of the whole picture of the sustainable supply of clean water, playing our part in taking care to use it wisely.

TESTING BEFORE TASTING

After flowing through the water treatment works the drinking supply must be tested at various points along the route to our domestic taps. This is carried out rigorously and in accordance with government directives. The Drinking Water Inspectorate independently assesses and tests these results.

Yorkshire Water has fifty-five treatment plants in order to meet the standards, and regular samples are taken from the 359 service reservoirs where treated water is stored and also from time to time, the taps in peoples' homes.

The legal standards for drinking water in the UK are those which were set by the Drinking Water Directive of 1998, together with national standards set to maintain our high quality of water. The standards are strict and cover the count of bacteria, chemicals such as nitrate and pesticides, metals such as lead and copper. Finally, the appearance of the water and how it tastes are very important to us, the consumer.

REFERENCES

www.britishdowsers.com Accessed 19.2.19

Hunt, Clare. 'X marks the spot', Countryside NFU magazine. October 2016.

Sheffield Water Supply (https://www.yorkshirewater.com/sheffieldwater) Accessed 12.1.19

Vickers, Edward. A Popular History of Sheffield. Applebaum Bookshop publishing Ltd Sheffield. Revised 1987. ISBN 0-906787-04-1

'The Water Supply to Sheffield and District'. Sheffield Water Undertaking 1968.

https://www.yorkshirewater.com/sheffieldwater Accessed 10.3.19.

Picture taken early one morning of a water worker extracting a sample from Rudd Hill underground service reservoir, Lodge Moor.

Chapter 1 - Dire Disasters.

EYAM'S STORY

MOMPESSON'S WELL – PHILANTHROPY IN ACTION

The little village of Eyam in Derbyshire is famous for a disaster which struck in 1665 when it was visited by the Plague. 260 of its 350 inhabitants died. However, their sacrifice of isolating themselves prevented the spread of this terrible disease to others both nearby and far away. The Reverend William Mompesson's foresight and bravery was responsible for this amazing accomplishment.

The water to the Mompesson well was supplied by a running stream, not a spring or well. It was once used to supply water for packhorses travelling on the road nearby. There were several troughs in the village of Eyam in the 15th and 16th centuries which were used to supply the households in the village.

The Mompesson well is situated a little way from one of the two entry roads into Eyam village. This packhorse way formed part of the 'Old Salt Route' between Sheffield and Cheshire. Salt was very important as it preserved meat during the winter.

Mompesson's Well - coins can be thrown into the water

Eyam was infected with the Plague between 1665 and 1666. It arrived in Eyam in a bale of cloth from London. The Reverend William Mompesson and the villagers took the very brave step of keeping to themselves and after the first few days letting no-one out of the village in order to save the neighbouring villages from becoming contaminated.

He developed a system of dropping food off from the surrounding villages for the residents of Eyam at the Mompesson well, and also at another site further way.

The residents of Eyam left coins below the water in the shallow well by way of payment for the food and I think this is an early example of the consideration of water to be sterilising or at least purifying in its effects.

At the other drop-off point, on the moor on the second road out of Eyam, a few holes were drilled in a rock into which vinegar was poured, again with the idea that it may 'sterilise' the coins used to pay for food.

The villagers eventually came through their ordeal, which continues to be remembered as an example of courage, care and common sense.

REFERENCE

https://www.historylearningsite.co.uk/stuart-england/eyam-and-the-great-plague-of-1665/ Accessed 15.5.19

Chapter 2 - Dire Disasters.

DR JOHN SNOW AND CHOLERA

Dr John Snow was born in 1813 into a poor hardworking family in York. As a child he frequently experienced flooding of the river Ouse which was near their home. He had a bright mind and his father worked hard to afford his studies. He took up various medical apprenticeships, the first of which was in Newcastle, where he witnessed cases of cholera in miners there. Another Apprenticeship was in Pateley Bridge, North Yorkshire, where he acquired the art of being an Apothecary (today's GP). He learned about communities and peoples' habits.

He was motivated by desire to improve peoples' lives by studying their situations. In effect this was early epidemiology.

Once trained, John Snow became an obstetrician but retained his interest in the cause of infectious disease. He had long believed that cholera, a very severe form of gastroenteritis, was caused by drinking water contaminated with sewage. He published an article in 1849 explaining his theory but was not acknowledged by the medical and scientific profession, as they all subscribed to the popular theory of 'miasma' (vapours or bad air) causing cholera. However, John Snow remained fairly convinced that sewage dumped into the river or into cesspools near town wells and their pumps could contaminate the drinking water supply and lead to a rapid spread of disease.

The Broad Street Pump as it is today (replica).

In 1854 Soho a suburb of London, was hit hard by a particularly intense and localised outbreak of cholera. Dr. Snow himself lived near Soho and immediately went to work to prove his theory that contaminated water was the cause of the outbreak. He noticed that there were around 500 fatal cases of cholera in homes in the vicinity of the large communal pump on Broad Street (now called Broadwick Sreet).

John Snow then concentrated on proving his theory. Using hospital and public records on timing of outbreaks, whether the victims drank water from the Broad Street pump and a geographical grid to chart deaths from the disease, he investigated each case to determine access to the pump water. Snow developed what he considered positive proof that the pump was the source of the epidemic. Negative evidence was as useful as positive: for example, a nearby workhouse had no cases of cholera because it drew water from its own, uncontaminated well.

On 7 September 1854, Snow took his research to the town officials and convinced them to take the handle off the pump. This they reluctantly did and the outbreak of cholera almost immediately came to a halt.

Broad Street (now called Broadwick Street).

Despite this obvious success of Snow's theory, public officials still thought his hypothesis was nonsense. The Board of Health refused to do anything to clean up the cesspools and sewers. It seemed to them a task too large and too expensive.

Not to be defeated, John Snow continued to track every case of cholera from the 1854 Soho outbreak and traced almost all of them back to the pump, including a cabinetmaker who was passing through the area and children who lived closer to other pumps but walked by the Broad Street pump on their way to school.

What he could not prove was where the contamination came from in the first place.

The mystery might never have been solved had a minister, Reverend Henry Whitehead, not taken on the task of proving Snow wrong. The minister contended that the outbreak was due to God's divine intervention. However, his theory could not be proved and his published report confirmed Snow's findings. Its crowning achievement was to give Snow the probable solution to the cause of the pump's contamination.

Reverend Whitehead had interviewed a woman who lived at 40 Broad Street, whose child had contracted cholera from some other source. The child's mother had washed the baby's nappies in water which she then dumped into a leaky cesspool just three feet from the Broad Street pump. This was the source of the devastating epidemic.

Gradually, following this, public services and builders applied some pressure for the construction of reliable non-leaking sewers in order to drain contaminated water. This was driven by the fear of another epidemic if a source could not be addressed. Sadly it still took many years for adequate development to take place.

However, it was spurred on by Dr Robert Koch in Germany. In 1883 he discovered the bacterium Vibrio cholerae, the cause of cholera. Dr. Koch determined that cholera was spread through unsanitary water or food supply sources - a major victory for Snow's theory. The cholera epidemics in Europe and the United States in the 19th century ended after cities finally improved water supply sanitation.

The cholera story serves to show that even in the face of extensive and convincing evidence to the contrary, London's sanitary authorities of the time brushed off this theory for over a decade after the outbreak, maintaining their stance that air ('miasma') was the cause of disease. In peoples' eyes bad smelly air was more likely to transmit disease than clear-looking water, but in fact the reverse was true. How it appeared was not necessarily a marker of water quality - the clear water from the pump could bring death.

It took twelve years before work started to remove old cesspools and sewers and replace them with watertight new ones. Use of street water pumps declined. Instead it became the responsibility of Water Companies to ensure water availability to homes at a good quality.

The John Snow pub, Soho, next to the replica Broad Street pump

The World Health Organisation estimates 78 percent of the people in developing countries are still without clean water supplies today. Up to 85 percent of those people do not live in areas with adequate sewage treatment, making cholera outbreaks an ongoing concern in some parts of the world.

REFERENCES

Jones, Emma. Parched City. Zero Books, Winchester UK. 2012. ISBN 978 1 78099 158 0

Sharp Liz. Reconnecting People with Water. Public engagement and sustainable urban water management. Earthscan, Routledge. 2017. ISBN 978 0 415 72845 4

Hempel, Sandra. The Lancet published: April 13, 2013 DOI:https://doi.org/10.1016/S0140-6736(13)60830-2 Accessed 19.1.19.

Chapter 3 - Dire Disasters.

DALE DYKE DISASTER

How a dam burst its banks in 1864, Sheffield

Friday 11th March 1864 was a particularly stormy day. The weather forecast warned of strong gales and because of this Mr Gunson the Sheffield Water Works Company's resident engineer came to inspect it. He found the water level three inches below the top of the embankment at 3pm but otherwise all appeared safe. At 5.30pm a workman, William Horsfield, employed by the SWC had to cross the embankment to get to his home, but the wind was so strong that this was impossible and he had to take a different route. As he did so he noticed a crack about 12 feet from the top of the dam and running for 50 yards but he wasn't particularly concerned as he had seen this happen before in winter. However, he mentioned it to another workman called Greaves who then told Samuel Hammerton who was a farmer living nearby. He went to look and was alarmed so he told a man called Swinden who was one of the SWWC's overlookers. By now it was 7pm and nearly dark. Mr Swinden and several others took their lanterns and gathered around but by then the wind was at gale strength, the waves dashing against the dam and the crack was widening by the minute. They decided to send one of their sons, Stephenson Fountain, on horseback to tell Mr Gunson, while they opened sluice gates to try to reduce the pressure of water.

The young man was level with Damflask, about two miles away, when his saddle-girth broke and he turned in at the Barrel Inn for it to be repaired. He told the landlord about the dam and the several men who were in the pub at the time. However, no-one suspected the danger, but I think they took note of his warning. He set off again and reached Mr Gunson at around 9pm, who then set off in pony and trap to the dam. While he was hurrying up there, he saw some people driving their cattle up the hill and even moving their families away. These were the ones who had heeded Stephenson's tale.

Mr Gunson and his engineer Mr Craven immediately realised the danger when they saw the widening crack. Before they could take any further measures to try to reduce pressure on the dam the water forced its way through and they had to run for their lives. The bank then collapsed within seconds and 114 million cubic feet of water cascaded down the valley, sweeping away all in its path, destroying bridges and houses and tearing rocks from the ground, one even weighing 60 tons.

Henry Whittle's house damaged in the Flood. The family of seven made a miraculous escape.
Courtesy of Sheffield Library and Philip Robinson,
a relative of the Whittle family, with grateful thanks.

Some families had had warning, taken heed and escaped, whereas others were less fortunate. Most people in Low Bradfield escaped but the death toll was high in Malin Bridge further down. Onwards in its path, Owlerton suffered great loss and in the city centre where many industries were destroyed – Kelham Island and Neepsend, even up to the Midland Railway Station. It continued its trail of destruction through Rotherham but eventually petered out on its way to Doncaster.

It was at the time, the greatest tragedy that England had ever known. Seven hundred million gallons of water took with it 270 lives,

798 destroyed homes, 693 animals and 15 stone bridges. The SWWC did not deny their liability for the damage and after a long process of assessment of the losses, the company paid a total of £373,000 in compensation. However, water charges to the public went up by 25% following that. The Dale Dyke dam was rebuilt in 1875.

Some time after, the SWWC was bought out by the City Council by compulsory purchase and an Act of Parliament, in 1888.

The whole disaster was chronicled in detail by a Sheffield printer, Samuel Harrison, who published the tale the very next day in the Sheffield Telegraph, the town's first daily paper established in 1856.

Flood graves can also be seen in the graveyard of Loxley United Reformed Church (known locally as Loxley Chapel) dating from 1787, which awaits restoration.

REFERENCES

Lightowler, Karen. Sheffield Flood – The Aftermath. 4th Edition, Jan 2018. E-sales product ID 23472178.

Vickers, Edward. A Popular History of Sheffield. 1992. Applebaum Publishing. ISBN 0-906787-04-1.

Amey, Geoffrey. The Collapse of the Dale Dyke Dam, 1864. Accessed 26.5.19 at -

http://www.mick-armitage.staff.shef.ac.uk/sheffield/book/Dale%20Dyke%20Dam%20(Collapse%20of).txt

Harrison, S. A Complete History of the Great Flood at Sheffield on March 11 & 12, 1864. First published Samuel Harrison. London and Sheffield 1864. Republished 1974 Evans & Longley Associates, Dewsbury.

Sharp, L. Reconnecting People and Water – Public Engagement and Sustainable Urban Water management. Earthscan (Routledge) 2017. ISBN 978 0415 72845

Above: Dale Dyke commemorative stone next to the dam.

Right: The Rose Inn public house, Penistone Road, was used as a temporary mortuary.

Flood grave in St Nicholas Church, High Bradfield.

Chapter 4 - Dire Disasters.

CARSINGTON WATER

Carsington Water

JS~2019

landslip occurred nearby, putting pressure on the crack which then sprung apart, but fortunately before it was filled with water. Although it was the largest geotechnical failure of a structure within the UK it did not carry the killing-power of Dale Dyke.

The specialist Civil Engineers made a thorough investigation, concluding that the clay core was at fault, and rebuilding it all in a different manner. It was completed in eight years. The reservoir was finally opened by the Queen in 1992. It is subject to regular surveillance by the engineers.

This beautiful stretch of water is now home to many types of wildlife, as well as supplying opportunities for sailing, windsurfing, cycling, walking, fishing and birdwatching.

Carsington Dam lies at one end of Carsington Water, an important reservoir in Derbyshire, taking water from the River Derwent and the many surrounding hills (it holds as much water as Ladybower and Upper Derwent reservoirs together). It is the responsibility of Severn Trent Water and is the ninth largest reservoir in England, supplying water to over three million people in Derbyshire, Nottinghamshire and Leicestershire. Construction of the dam started in 1979.

However, the dam was to befall a (fortunate) misfortune. In the early hours of 4th June 1984, after a couple of weeks of heavy rainfall, and shortly before the reservoir as due to be filled, a crack appeared running along the crest of the dam wall. A few hours later, a

REFERENCE

https://www.ice.org.uk/what-is-civil-engineering/what-do-civil-engineers-do/carsington-dam-reconstruction
Accessed 24.4.19

Chapter 1 - Worrying Waste.
WILLIAM GIBBS OF GUANO FAME (1790 – 1875)

William Gibbs was born into a family who traded in wool. He initially joined his father's business in Spain then moved to Bristol where he was a clerk for his uncle's firm. The family next formed a new London trading company, Anthony Gibbs and Son, where William became a partner in1813. He moved to Spain trading in food as well as wool and then transferred the business to the Pacific coast of South America. In the 1830's he became wealthy and put this to good use supporting the British railways and the Church. His knowledge of food production led him to consider farming practices and fertiliser.

Up to mid-1800's farmers were using 'night soil' (the contents of domestic middens) as well as cow manure to fertilise their crops. This became unsustainable in the face of a rapidly growing need for food.

A manure heap on a Cumbrian farm.
Photo: J R B Deane

William Gibbs procured a precious commodity for Britain and at the same time supplied a solution to the domestic midden.

The Government of Peru in 1842 signed a contract with the Gibbs family business to collect guano from the coasts of their islands. Guano was the birdlime of sea birds which collected there and became baked in the hot climate. It was an excellent source of concentrated nitrogen and phosphorus which could be made into fertiliser. Gone was the need for 'night soil' back in Britain.

In 1856, a total of 211,000 tons of guano were imported via the ports of Bristol and London. Their nitrogen content, however, made the cargo explosive when it came into contact with sea water, and dock workers had to be reminded to stack the boxes on bricks so that air could circulate.

Therefore the letters were stamped on the boxes – 'Store High in Transit'.

(However, the familiar word is not derived from the guano meaning. The former comes from a Middle English word 'shytte').

The guano importing business came to an end in 1880 as stocks became depleted and the Gibbs business moved to Chile where it manufactured nitrate of soda and iodine. These were used in the production of fertiliser as well as munitions.

William Gibbs lived with his family in the great Victorian Gothic house Tyntesfield near Bristol, which is now owned by the National Trust and may be visited. He sold his business to his nephew Henry Gibbs in 1843, who moved the business from provender and guano to merchant banking into the nineteenth century.

Tyntesfield after its restoration in 2011
Photo: Gillian Rowcliffe 2019 with grateful thanks

REFERENCES

The Oxford Dictionary of National Biography. Copyright Oxford University Press. 2019.

https://www.oxforddnb.com/view/10.1093/ref:odnb/9780198614128.001.0001/odnb-9780198614128-e-89656?atitle=Tyntesfield%2C+Somerset&aulast=Hall&date=2002-04-25&epage=117&genre=article&sid=oup%3Aorr&spage=114&title=Country+Life

Accessed 8.6.19.

Chapter 2 - Worrying Waste.

THE SEWER REVOLUTION

SEWERS FLOWING FROM PAST TO FUTURE STARTING IN LONDON

The London sewer system has had to serve the multiplying population of our industrial capital. It developed from a rudimentary ad-hoc construction of separate channels and cesspools and the dirty water frequently came into contact with the clean water meant for drinking. We have seen in previous chapters the consequences of this.

A solution was to unfold with Joseph Bazalgette, detailed in Section 5, chapter 6.

In 1860, this tough and talented engineer made the first centralised sewerage system for London, then a city of two million people. The coming of the domestic toilet demanded the development of sewers to connect and remove waste. This involved much planning with the authorities, mindful that sewage must be kept out of the Thames. Each sewer was dug out by teams of men. This was hard work in the heavy London clay. They were then lined with brick, secured using Portland cement, four to five metres underground. They were so well built that they were still in good order 150 years later. The earth dug out to create the sewers was tipped into the side of the Thames (called Embankment) in order to reclaim land on which to build the lowest level 'interceptor' sewer. This collected sewage from the surrounding 450 miles (720 km) of main sewers and in turn from 13,000 miles (21,000 km) of smaller sewers. Due to Bazalgette's oval cross-sectional shape of the sewer tunnels and gently angled joins, there was less likelihood of blockage.

Embankment reclaimed 22 acres (89,000 m²) of land from the river. It helped to prevent flooding, provided space for the increasing traffic and also housed a part of the underground railway.

London possibly gained the idea from Liverpool. Their Council built a water supply and sewer system (all 250 miles of it) starting in 1847 taking them twenty years to complete. About five percent of a council tenant's annual rent was levied for this privilege so it didn't come cheap. Doulton of stoneware fame was called upon to produce salt glazed stoneware drainpipes leading to the sewers which were less likely to block up, and success flowed.

As well as sewerage, these constructions have to cope with surface water run-off from roads and land. If there is a flood caused by the fall of intense rain, as we are finding in current times, then the sewers can overflow, causing a health hazard. In some cities like Sheffield large Storm Drains were built in order to take away this surface water separately. Sheffield's Megatron is a remarkable Victorian example, built in the 1860's. It is possible to visit it but a guide is needed.

Inside the entrance to Sheffield's Megatron (storm drain, not sewer). Photo with grateful thanks to Brian Holmshaw.

THE DRAINAGE DILEMMA

London is now home to nine million people and more than one million tonnes of raw sewage is produced daily, some of it once again entering the Thames untreated. In the mix is a modern hazard – that of 'wet-wipes' thrown down the toilet rather than into waste

> Think about our poor old drains (and the poor fella who has to clean 'em out!)
> **Don't put Nappies, Sanitary Towels or Paper Towels down the loo.**
> Please use the bags provided and put 'em in the bin

bins. They are fibrous and do not dissolve. They become impaled on matter in the sewers and form hanging 'curtains' which have to be cleared manually.

The modern sewer-worker has also become familiar with the 'fatberg' especially in areas where there are restaurants. The fat accumulated whilst cooking is tipped down the drains and solidifies in contact with cold water. It immediately forms a voluminous sticky mass to which other debris adheres, magnifying the problem. Domestic grease in this quantity needs to be allowed to cool in the kitchen then put when solid into the waste bin.

Please don't flush.

Nappies, sanitary towels, paper towels, gum.

Old phones, unpaid bills, junk mail, your ex's sweater, hopes, dreams or goldfish.

Down this toilet.

In a sewer, you are never far from a rat.

Graffiti seen on a town wall in Lucca, Italy.

THE SEWER SOLUTION

There is a £5 billion London project to dig a tunnel twenty miles long and 23 feet (7 metres) wide (the width of three London buses). Work commenced in 2015. The proposed mega-sewer is to lie deeper than the Tube and follow the Thames, one lead tunnel from Acton running through to Beckton (by then 262 feet, or 80 metres underground). At Beckton there will be Europe's largest Treatment Works, situated in East London. There will be two shafts downwards, one at Battersea and the other at Tower Bridge. This feat of civil engineering should be completed by 2023.

Sheffield's Blackburn Meadows Waste Water Treatment Plant (WWTW)

Sheffield's sewers carried their contents out to the east of the city where this plant was built as long ago as 1884. The mix of sewage and rainwater running off roads, sometimes with pollutants, was collected into the thirty precipitating tanks. Here, the solid matter gravitated to the bottom, and the floating matter such as oil from industries was scooped from the top. Lime was used in the process, too. The next step involved holding the water in sixty aerating tanks, during which time bacteria broke down the sewage. Then the water was filtered through gravel. The remaining 'sewage sludge' was used as fertiliser, and the watery remains were discharged into the river Don. However, the lime in the process was exchanged for a biological process in 1905.

It subsequently underwent further upgrades to make the sewerage treatment process more efficient and the effluent more biodegradable as technology progressed, in 1914, 1956, 1969, 1979, 1983 and 1992.

Blackburn Meadows WWTW is one of the largest sewerage works in Yorkshire. The site is now 78 acres and it treats waste water from over 800,000 people as well as some industrial sites. In 2012 it underwent a £78 million development to cater for increasing population, improve water quality in the Don and become less environmentally damaging.

An Ill Wind Can Blow Good

Sewage lets off a gas called methane. This is a flammable gas, a simple 'alkane' of the Hydrocarbon group of gases, comprising carbon and hydrogen (CH_4). It comes off during the processing of sewage due to anaerobic decomposition of organic material. It has to be discharged as otherwise it may explode.

In Sheffield there are several streetlights, in Nether Edge and Broomhill, for example, which run off sewer gas.

Streetlight on Park Lane, Broomhill, which runs off methane from the sewers.

Photo: with grateful thanks to T. Stephenson.

There can be seen what appears to be a very tall drainpipe pointing skywards on a street in Cambridge next to the river. It was erected in the Victorian era for discharging methane and smells from the sewers, high up so that it did not offend the sensitive noses of the residents.

Another type of methane discharge pipe is seen next to some of the houses along the streets of the small town of Buckingham. The short pipe faces forwards at the top, covered by a vent. They are generally next to the front door, so no smoking!

REFERENCES

http://www.open.edu/openlearn/tv-radio-events/tv/the-five-billion-pound-super-sewer Accessed 24.7.18 and 10.6.19.

https://www.yorkshirewater.com/household/services/waste-water

Sharp, L. Reconnecting People and Water. Earthscan, Routledge 2017. ISBN 978-0-415-72845-4.

https://www.28dayslater.co.uk/threads/megatron-sheffield-june-and-july-2015.97955/ Accessed 12.6.19.

http://www.dailymail.co.uk/news/article-3177399/What-lurks-beneath-Incredible-underground-pictures-network-Victorian-storm-drains-city-Sheffield.html Accessed 12.6.19.

https://www.yorkshirewater.com/saltend Accessed 12.6.19.

Chapter 3 - Worrying Waste.

VICTORIAN WATER PUMPING STATIONS

With the increasing population, the UK saw the best of Victorian engineering surge into action once again, in the form of magnificent water pumping stations. The buildings alone were enough to take one's breath away, appearing like gothic cathedrals, mediaeval castles, magnificent Italianate houses, each with a chimney because they were steam-powered. These pumping stations were absolutely key to the 'sewerage revolution' which had to take place. They were then used to pump mains drinking water to the population or remove sewage into underground cisterns for treatment.

Views of the Victorian pump house at Ryhope, Sunderland. Built in 1868 to supply domestic water. It ceased operation in 1967 after 100 years of continuous use. It is now a museum and a visitor can see a demonstration of the two beam engines in action.
Photo by a good friend, with thanks

The first of these magnificent pumps was used by the Chelsea Waterworks Company in order to supply clean drinking water to the Royal Palaces. There had been a severe water shortage in 1739 and so a Newcomen steam engine was installed to ensure the flow of royal drinking water for the future.

Prior to this, the pumping stations had been built to drain agricultural land and improve production of crops. An important role was also to top up water in canals to keep commercial traffic on the move, and to supply the hydraulic systems that powered industrial machinery.

The skills of engineers such as Thomas Newcomen and James Watt brought into being the powerful pump mechanisms, and combined with inventers of boilers, safety improved and the pumping mechanism became more efficient.

Nineteenth -century Cambridge was awash with water problems, with the river Cam being increasingly contaminated, and typhoid and cholera becoming prevalent. Thanks to a campaigner, Eglantyne Jebb, pressure was put on the authorities and the sewage pumping station was built on Riverside in 1894. It pumped sewage out of the city away from clean water sources in order to be treated. It was used non-stop until 1968.

View of pumping house chimney, Cambridge.
Photo: L Stephenson with grateful thanks.

Each station comprised the Engine House which needed to be tall and strong like a fortified castle in order to house and hold the heavy machinery; the Boiler House for the boilers which, with a steady supply of coal created the steam with which to power the pumps; and an elegant chimney (most of which were removed prior to World War 2 for safety reasons) in order to draw down fresh air for the boilers and relieve the station of smoke. As well as these, a works and a forge were required for ongoing repairs, and of course housing for the Foreman and his staff. The main pumps powered by the engines were sited below the floor of the Engine House.

These 'temples to cleanliness' provided an essential function but were disguised by the fastidious Victorians by their admirable architecture.

REFERENCES

Yorke, T. Victorian Pumping Stations. Shire Publications, Bloomsbury publishing plc. 2018. ISBN 978 1 78442 268 4

https://www.telegraph.co.uk/news/2016/08/15/victorian-pumping-station-dubbed-the-cistern-chapel-is-turned-in/ Accessed 1.5.19

http://www.creatingmycambridge.com/history-stories/cambridge-museum-of-technology/

Chapter 4 - Worrying Waste.

THE THOROUGHLY MODERN MIDDEN

'Midden' is an Old English word for a heap of dung or a cesspit used for human waste. Later, it was also used to refer to a collection of general household rubbish. It was the 'bread and butter' of a homestead for many centuries until Thomas Crapper came up with the idea of a more elegant and discreet solution.

The flush toilet has become a sign of civilisation. Over the centuries it has collected various names, from 'Lavatory', Loo, 'Water Closet' or W.C., 'Bog', 'Privy', and from America – 'Bathroom' which is a somewhat coy expression increasingly used throughout Europe. 'Restroom' is another. I have variously heard 'Little Girls'/Boys' Room', 'The Plumbing', 'The Throne Room' and 'Pissoir'.

It is hygienic because the water in the bowl (the 'water closet') forms an effective seal between the toilet and the drain and it affords a convenient way of cleanly getting rid of waste. However, environmentally, it is not ideal because with each flush, a considerable amount of water is in effect wasted, from between two litres and 7.5 litres depending on the type of toilet. This could have a significant impact in parts of the world where water is very scarce.

Toilet flushing is the largest single use of water in households and this has a definite environmental impact. The toilet is designed to collect dirty water ('black' water) which has to be cleaned. It leads to the generation of around twenty million tonnes of sewage sludge in the UK, which is as much as all other household refuse.

In order to consider alternatives to the standard toilet our preconceptions about it need to be flushed away and innovative and ecologically-based solutions be considered. These involve a biological process and the toilets are referred to as 'dry'.

CURIOUS AND CARBONIFEROUS NATURE

Ninety-five percent of living things are made up of water and carbon dioxide. Plants build up complex organic matter from these, plus a few minerals like nitrogen from the water, using energy from sunlight. This leaves oxygen as a by-product. After that, combining organic matter with oxygen releases energy and makes carbon dioxide water and minerals again. This is referred to as the Carbon-Energy cycle, and its processes are balanced. Most decomposition processes involve the latter part of the cycle, breaking down organic matter into water and oxygen, releasing heat. This forms the basis of the 'biological' toilet. It may not degrade completely but leave a 'humus' which is odourless, clean and very valuable for soil quality. The breakdown process is driven by decomposer organisms, aerobic bacteria, which are stimulated by heat and the nutrients and oxygen.

THE MODERN DRY TOILET

The waste from the toilet does contain the other sort of bacteria, anaerobic ones, which thrive if there isn't much oxygen. They putrify and make a smell. The 'biological' toilet aims to avoid conditions of low oxygen so the toilet waste is mixed with other things like sawdust, paper or earth to make it lighter so the oxygen can penetrate.

A nineteenth century midden containing straw as seen at Styal Mill, near Manchester Airport 2018. It worked on the same principles as the modern variety.

The whole system needs to be well drained so that aeration can take place. It is 'poisoned' by chemicals such as detergents and disinfectants so these must not be added to a dry toilet.

The biological waste is collected and left for anything up to a year to turn into compost by the cycle described above, and the action of worms and some rainwater. Most of the germs which could cause illness are slowly killed by the generated heat but the resulting compost is not recommended for use on food crops.

Nick Parsons of Sustainable Building, Sheffield, has made these notes possible, and has a message about ecological sustainability which should not be ignored. It should be taken into account for the future. He endorses a 'wheelie bin' type of arrangement for collection of waste which is then left for a year or more to compost and 'cleanse' itself.

The outdoor dry toilet.

Photo courtesy of Nick Parsons, Sustainable Building.

In the June 2019 edition of Countryside magazine, there is advertised the 'Temple to Nature' dry toilet, (complete with a bird box, and water store for garden use), which can also be used as a birdwatching hide!

THE SEPTIC TANK

Another sewage system is the not-so-modern septic tank, which dates from about 1860, though modern forms of it are used nowadays. Waste enters at one end and the solids sink to the bottom (which may have to be removed periodically), while the liquid passes to another chamber and leaves the tank. It then runs through porous underground pipes called a leachfield and from there percolates into the soil. The sewage is then considered to have been treated. Advice must be sought from the Environment Agency before considering using these methods, as several regulations will apply.

An old lady lived in the countryside and one year her septic tank overflowed into the lower part of her vegetable patch. She had it pumped out, but the next year she had a bumper crop of peas. Her family came for lunch one day, and they found her rinsing the peas in Dettol!

Harking back to the olden days of the Privy, we can see some similarities and a big difference. Toilet waste was collected without additional water other than that of urine and then sometimes a little earth (as in 'earth closet') was sprinkled over to deter flies and smells. When full, the contents were dug out by the 'night soil men'. This was not an enviable job as it was wet and heavy as the old privies had a 'cesspit' underneath which held the wet sewage. This wetness is what prevented the aerobic break-down and helped infections like cholera to spread. The sewage was taken for manure on farms, which could compound the problems of infection spread. There, however, it would eventually break down in the open air in the way described for the biological toilet.

REED BEDS – THE WATER FILTERING SOLUTION

The reed bed is a biological system for cleansing water supplies. Reeds and other wetland plants have root structures which are adapted to anaerobic conditions, where there is little oxygen, due to the soil being waterlogged. These sorts of plants are very good at trapping and detoxifying heavy metals, chemical pollutants such as petrol derivatives and any toxic waste in materials such as sewage. The process happens by using the microbes in the roots to trap them and bind them chemically.

A famous use of such a natural filtration bed is at Highgrove House on the Duchy Estate where Prince Charles' organic and environmental philosophy is seen in the treatment of waste and promotion of sustainability.

CHINA'S WASTE PROBLEM (2013)

China faces an unpleasant problem – that of mounting waste. Increasing population density has meant a deepening amount of sewage, which has posed a health and an environmental threat. Drinking water is constantly at risk of pollution.

China has 7% of the world's water resources but 22% of the world's population. The use of pesticides and chemicals has increased food production but caused pollution of water and environment. Compounding that, the intensive production of meat has caused increased water usage and pollution, especially the rearing of pigs which excrete large amounts of phosphates into the groundwater.

The tide is now turning.

New laws have been passed and experts from all over the world have drawn up a five-year sustainability plan involving more sewerage systems. China now has the world's second-highest sewerage processing capacity, The plan also involves making more efficient re-use of wastewater by recycling, and replacing piping and infrastructure. History is repeating itself – treated human waste is now being used as agricultural fertiliser. Biological processes are employed as well as anaerobic digesters. 'Constructed wetlands' are effective as an ecological alternative wastewater treatment method and pollutant extraction and cost half as much as traditional methods.

REFERENCES

I am very grateful to Nick Parsons of Sustainable Building for his advice on dry toilets and waste systems.

http://syec.co.uk/sustainable/ Accessed 8.6.19. Sustainable Building.

Harper, P and Halestrap, L . 'Lifting the Lid – An ecological approach to toilet systems'. The Centre for Alternative Technology, UK. CAT Publications 1999. ISBN 1 898049 79 3

Also https://natsol.co.uk/ Accessed 5.6.19.

www.templetonature@icloud.com

https://www.waterworld.com/international/waste water/article/16201297/chinas-13th-five-year-plan-what-role-will-wastewater-play Accessed 5.6.19.

Chapter 5 - Worrying Waste

TOILET TIMELINE

Man has always lived with the fact that getting rid of waste determines his comfort, health and quality of life. The toilet itself has evolved alongside him but its timeline has been punctuated by trial and error, ignorance and inventiveness.

One of the earliest records of quite sophisticated toilets was in Ancient Egypt, with limestone toilet seats being found in the tombs of the Pharaohs, as in this photograph I took while visiting the British Museum in 2015.

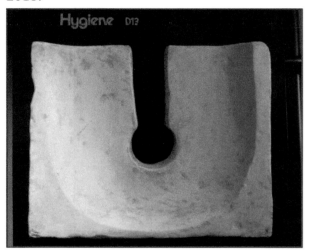

The Ancient Egyptians also had plumbing and sewers. The ancient Romans were similarly highly developed with their water systems.

There were public toilets in their public baths, as in Section 2, Chapter 1. They used sponges on sticks for cleaning after using the toilet, which were kept in a jar of salt water ready for the next user. They were regularly cleaned as well.

In mediaeval times the toilets were usually of midden type (see earlier in this section), and the drainage was variable as well - either into open gullies running down the middle of the main road or leaking wooden cesspits. The 'guarderobe' was the privy of a castle, built on the side high up and letting the waste drop directly down onto the enemy or into the river below.

This excellently-preserved example is from the Marmion Tower at West Tanfield, near Ripon, North Yorkshire.

Otherwise, most people relied on the bedpan or chamber pot which was convenient for overnight use and emptied out of the window next morning.

This example to the right, again a photo of mine from the British Museum in 2015, shows a bedpan from about 1700.

This smart version is a decorated Dutch chamber pot from the 18th century.

The one to the right is a plain ceramic chamber pot in its cupboard from later 19th century France, discovered in a creaky old house in Toulouse in 2015.

The flushing toilet then took over from the middens, cesspits, chamber pots and earth and ash closets. The first known inventor of the flushing toilet was Sir John Harington (1561 – 1612), a poet, who made a bowl with a leather valve and a filling cistern above. He was godson to Queen Elizabeth I who ordered one for herself in 1592; however this new-fangled contraption didn't become popular.

In the nineteenth century, however, the flushing toilet came into its own, after the first patent had been taken out for a water closet in 1775 by Alexander Cummings, a London horologist. This was considerably improved by Joseph Bramah in 1778 and therefore the commodes disguised as handsome chairs (as the one above, courtesy of Mary Grover) became confined to bedrooms.

Joseph Bramah (1748 – 1814) was best known as an ingenious locksmith and the inventor of the hydraulic press. He came from near Barnsley, South Yorkshire. He invented the double valve closet which sealed off smells and also spread the incoming water all around the toilet bowl which was much cleaner. He produced a syphon system which ensured the upper pipework was empty when not in use in order to prevent freezing up.

The photograph shows the excellent example of the Bramah Flushing Pan Closet discovered in 2005 when the Butchers Wheel old cutlery works was being renovated. The pull-up handle released a hinged valve (suitably decorated with a Yorkshire rose), dropping the contents of the bowl. At the same time water runs down into the pan from the cistern above, washing the bowl and renewing the water seal when the valve has closed.

The Bramah was the best type of toilet for a hundred years and became a status symbol.

The toilet pictured here (above) has a pull-up flush mechanism as invented by Bramah. I saw it in Nunnington Hall, North Yorkshire (complete with book to while away the hours).

Bramah ordered his ceramic bowls from Wedgwood which were decorated and pretty to look at as well as serviceable.

Thomas William Twyford produced the first W.C. in 1883 made all in one piece, and as such was extremely successful – the name is recognised today.

The life of Thomas Crapper is described in Section 5, when he set up business in 1861 in Marlborough Road, Chelsea, from where he developed in 1895 the Improved Marlborough wash-down W.C. This was lower and less depth front to back and was easier for the plumber to fix than other models.

The Bramah flushing closet in an old workshop, Butchers Wheel, Sheffield dating from around 1870 with water cistern above, lead downpipe having been partially removed.

PUBLIC TOILETS

The oldest Listed public toilets in the UK are at Lofthouse, in North Yorkshire.

They are simple in design and suitable for gentlemen, situated in a delightful village.

Victorians became mobile thanks to the steam train and other modes of public and personal transport. They liked to take holidays at places a little further away from their home towns, for example, at the coast. They needed public toilets and these were duly developed. Many of these no longer survive for us to see their large ceramic elegance and decorated pull-chains, but there are some notable preserved examples.

These beautiful toilets were built in 1899 next to Rothesay pier on the Scottish island of Bute. The photograph was taken by Dr J Deane and accepted with grateful thanks.

Below is another well preserved elegant set of gentle-men's Victorian toilets in Liverpool, dating from 1898, from what was once a Gentlemen's club. The photo is courtesy of a good friend, who took the trouble to trace them for me.

Many public toilets have unfortunately been closed due to financial pressures upon City Councils. If planning a journey with toilet facilities in mind, consult *https://www.toiletmap. org.uk/* for updated advice.

The public toilet next to the Town Hall in Sheffield is now a Bar called 'Public'.

Many City Councils support a scheme where by local businesses open their toilets to the public, and these display a toilet share sign.

In Sheffield centre there were toilets overhanging the river Don near Lady's Bridge. These are also being converted into a café.

In Bakewell, Derbyshire, the public toilets offer something for everyone (above photo).

TOILETS IN TROUBLE

During World War II, Air Raid Shelters were the refuge of the population, often for many hours at a time. In some tea was served by the WRVS. Most had some form of toilet arrangement.

This photograph shows the row of toilets inside the Air Raid Shelter of Stockport, in the borough of Greater Manchester.

The flush was at the end of the row; people lined up depending on need and there was a handwashing facility in the next room. A single sewer ran under the complex of tunnels.

ADAPTED TOILETS

These can be found in all sorts of places such as this one I saw in a tiny bathroom in a live-in horsebox (for the owner of the horse). It had a cassette, also pictured, designed to be removed from the outside for emptying.

Others include sea toilets which are generally found on small ocean-going boats, which discharge sewage untreated out into the sea. Inland boats such as barges have chemical toilets with a cassette to hold the material which is then emptied at a service station next to the canal.

This pretty little house is home to toilets and washrooms for the convenience of users of Ripon canal, North Yorkshire.

THE DAILY PAPER

Before the days of toilet paper, the Romans used sponges, Henry VIII used a flannel, and the people used handfuls of grass, hay, cotton waste – whatever was handy. In the nineteenth century, newspapers became available, torn into squares and hung up by the toilet for convenience.

cdp.co.uk

1863 saw the invention of purpose-made toilet paper, patented by F. Feichtinger. It came in a variety of sizes and was treated with eucalyptus , carbolic acid and pine oils in order to make it antiseptic. Rolled toilet paper was not made until 1878 when Scott Paper Company (Philadelphia) produced it, followed by entertaining ideas including the printing of jokes on it! Andrex (Kimberly-Clark) brought coloured paper onto the market in 1957, its original slogan being 'soft and strong and very, very long,' which has lasted until today running into the future.

A very ornate toilet as photographed by me in a London shop window in 2009.

REFERENCES

The Bramah Pan Closet was made available for me to visit, thanks to Carole Baugh, Cultural Producer, Freeman College (Ruskin Mill Trust), Sheffield Hallam University on 18.7.19.

Ragland, J. The Hidden Room – A Short History of the 'Privy'. Kingston University, Faculty of Art, Design and Music, New Design Centre, St. Pölten, Austria BA (Hons). Product and Furniture Design. February 2004

Lambton, L. Temples of Convenience and Chambers of Delight.2002.

Reyburn, W. Flushed with Pride. Macdonald, London. 1969. SBN 356 02995 6

Chapter 6 - Worrying Waste.

TOILET TALES AND OTHER FAMILY FORTUNES

TOILET TRICKS OF THE 1920's

In the 1920's a grandfather in our family, who enjoyed playing practical jokes, found that the toilet provided rich opportunity for causing inconvenience and dismay.

He developed the prank of 'danking the candle' whereby unbeknown to anyone, he would make a narrow channel in the side of the candle, angled downwards until it met the wick. He would then fill it with water and leave it where an unsuspecting family member would take it and light it in preparation for a dark journey down the garden path to use the privy in the night.

His skill was such that he could estimate how long it would take before the candle spluttered out, exactly timed to extinguish as the family member arrived at the privy. This caused aggravation and a few expletives as the victim haplessly felt around for the handle.

Once the family got wise to this trick, he developed another. This involved placing a broom up against the privy door, which fell onto the victim as they again sought the services of the privy on a dark night.

MOTHER IN THE 1930's

My 'aunt-in-law' always remembers her mother on a busy wash day. There was a strict routine. All the laundry was sorted into piles while the Copper heated up. This was a large copper bowl set in a brick kiln with a fire which she stoked underneath.

Once the water was nearly boiling, soap powder was sprinkled in and stirred with long wooden tongs. First, the whites and linens went in, including the Sunday-best tablecloths, She agitated them about and rubbed them then they were pulled out with the tongs and wrung out and set aside in a large bowl or the sink to await rinsing. Next, she put in the underwear, followed by shirts and dresses. After about an hour she emerged in a cloud of steam with rosy cheeks and shouted to the household - 'I've made a Good Water! Anything else to wash?' This was followed by the odd dirty sock, a forgotten apron and various other articles which were thrown into another pile. After she had processed these, she methodically went round her scullery cupboards and extracted the boot-polishing cloths and dusters, in order to 'use up' the Good Water.

Then the Copper was emptied and refilled with cold water and the fire extinguished. The rinsing process had begun.

This important weekly ritual was one of the pivots of family life in the 1930's. Now we hardly think of it – we charge up our washing machines and turn to do something else.

A COTTAGE'S AMENITIES IN THE 1950'S

Ivan remembers his early water facilities with some concerns. Don't read this if you are of a nervous disposition!

"I married Sheila in 1953, and after living with my parents for a short while, we moved into a cottage adjacent to Marshall's Brickyard at Storrs Bridge (Loxley Valley). This cottage was 7 shillings and sixpence weekly rent. It was a one-bedroomed cottage with only a cold tap and stone sink. The toilet was a midden with two seats, small and large, with lids. Our toilet which we shared and cleaned was back to back with the Rolling Mills toilet which was used by five men which naturally got full sooner than ours.

The binmen used to come once a week to empty the toilet. If they missed a week, the toilet got that full that we used to have a stick in a water-filled jam jar so could use this to push over the pyramid of waste before sitting down.

It was not unusual to see rats running about at the bottom so on entering the toilet you would bang the lid down a few times.

I was sitting there doing my business with a candle lit in a jam jar, when the door flew open and it was my neighbour who said, 'I'm busting!' I said, 'Sit down Maureen and do what you have to!' So we sat there together. Next morning she couldn't apologise enough.

What a job for the binmen climbing through a little door and filling a tin bath with sewage!"

FAMILY HABITS – 1940's – 1950's

Susan tells a tale of her early toilet experiences.

"I was born at Low Road, Malin Bridge, Sheffield in the 1947/48 winter when the snow was waist high and my parents had to wait to have me christened. We had an outdoor lavatory and, though we left when I was three, I can still remember it – it was cold; overlooking the Rivelin Valley was not enough to recommend it.

One of my earliest memories involves an aunt saying she was 'going for a pee' (a phrase my sweet mother would never have used!). I was next to the loo, and lo and behold, there was a green pea floating in the toilet bowl. I can offer an explanation for this now, but for years this coloured my imagination and I regarded my aunt with wonder.

I was always constipated as a child, probably due to lack of roughage and the fact that I was very shy about using the lavatory. I realised that by the time I had a child of my own that my self-conscious mother had somehow instilled embarrassment in me.

The next home I had was a council house with a downstairs toilet in the porch – also very cold in winter. When I was small and constipated mum used to put boiling water down the loo to try to help me to be moved. I was threatened with a soap enema at one stage so mum must have been desperately worried.

Neither did the toilets in our primary school invite relaxed 'activity'. One day I braved them, but the school secretary was in there with a poor lad in the throes of diarrhoea. After seeing the great pile of crumpled newspapers they were using, I never ventured in again and waited till I got home! Not the ideal situation and I still remember the lad's name!

As I grew up, the constipation became a way of life. I could never use the communal Lavatories at High Storrs Grammar School for Girls and had to survive the day's lessons, a mile walk and two bus journeys to use our facilities at home. I remember a play the school put on about a Town Council affording new public conveniences. I was completely in the dark as part of the comic script mentioned 'Gents' Urnals' and of course the 'i' was never in the 'Urnals'.

I had Measles when I was two and the story goes that I had to stay in a curtained room to protect my eyes. My darling father had to work away from home at this time and came home to a mardy, spoiled, measle-covered child. Apparently he corrected me sternly - as much as a toddler could understand – and my recovery came on in leaps and bounds, and we could once again enjoy the walks up the Rivelin Valley in my high-slung pram and see the cows come home in the meadows across the valley.

Where we lived at Southey Green there was a waterworks reservoir. Of course none of us actually saw any water in it as it was out of bounds and in those days we did as we were told. I had lots of dreams about this place and it remains a mystery to me. I grew up thinking it was a 'reservoy' as that was the pronunciation at the time.

I made sure that my child had no problems within the home about regularity and openness about bodily functions. This should be encouraged and the norm for all children – and of course the right diets!

Whenever I am a little stressed I sometimes have dreams about the area where I grew up. They are vivid: encompassing the whole area – school, neighbours, and our pets. It's slightly different from the reality but always the same within the dream. A psychiatrist friend refers to it as 'unfinished business' but I can only relate that to my experiences in the outdoor loos!"

THE CHANGING WATER SCENES IN THE 1950's AND 60's

Mike was born in 1949, the year after the National Health Service was established. For his first three years, Mike lived with his father's family in Attercliffe, Sheffield, where they were relatively privileged to have one indoor toilet.

Due to financial pressures, they then moved to live with Mike's grandfather where the family of six relied on one outside toilet, which was austere but considered normal in those days. Mike remembers visiting this toilet as a dark and scary experience, with spiders and insects as unwanted companions and little squares of the News of the World as toilet paper. He tried to 'save himself' to go when at school, as the toilets there seemed more hospitable, being in a clean, well-lit separate block.

Bath times were memorable in that each family member had to take a bath once a week, whether it was considered needed or not, in the large tin (zinc) bath which was ceremonially removed from its hook on the cellar head and placed in the kitchen. It was filled with a little water using boiling kettles and cold water. The children went first, sometimes two at a time. Anyone could walk in and out of the kitchen during the process, which Mike found a little embarrassing as he grew up, but Mother got the privilege of having the door shut and entrance was forbidden. She generally got a change of water as well. Eventually, the bath was emptied into a small grate in the centre of the yard.

When the family moved to Parson Cross in 1960, Mike was relieved to find that the house had hot and cold running water. However, at 21 when he married, their house in Pitsmoor had no bathroom and only cold running water, so they moved a short way down the street to a better equipped home shortly after.

Mike remembers that drinking water ran brown regularly and supplies were often interrupted. People then were advised to boil it before use in food preparation and drinking. When the water was turned completely off a tank appeared at the end of each street to supply the homes. Mike remembers first seeing bottled water for sale in the shops in the 1980's.

TOILETS TO THE RESCUE!

Being vigilant about one's eliminations can sometimes pay dividends, as in the case of these two women in the 1970's.

Nina began to notice that she did not pass urine very often, and this spurred her on to attend her doctor. Kidney failure was diagnosed. She needed renal dialysis. At that time she passed urine perhaps once a week and she became used to this. When she had her kidney transplant her functions became normal which felt like a nuisance to her, and she became very particular about toilets – she would send friends in to gauge the cleanliness of a public loo before she dared enter. This was partly because she was on medication which suppressed graft rejection but which also made her more susceptible to infections.

Margaret has another comment. "I think I owe my life to the toilet. If it wasn't for my mother spotting that I was going to wee an awful lot one week at the age of fourteen, my Type 1 Diabetes may not have been diagnosed in time."

In the hazardous days of World War 2, some of Sheffield's hospitals including the Royal Infirmary and Northern General (then called 'City General' Hospital) were used for returning soldiers, many of whom had infected wounds. Penicillin was in its early days then, and very precious, subject to shortages until enough could be produced.

Fortunately, at least 50% of the penicillin given to a patient comes out in the urine. Therefore, the urine of the convalescent soldiers was collected and distilled in order to extract the penicillin, which was then re-used to cure another patient.

TOILETS TO TORMENT

Another story looks at toilets from a different angle.

"In my younger days as a 1970's old hippy, I lived in a squat in Holborn. It was an old house, probably an absolute fire trap, but we did not have Health & Safety in those days. At the top of the house was a tiny loo, as decrepit and ghastly as you can possibly imagine, which I used to scrub like mad but it was actually beyond saving. Anyway, one of the housemates had stuck a poem up on the back of the door, which one couldn't help reading whenever enthroned. It was pretty spine-chilling, and read:

'For God hath meant to give Thee the Alarm,
When Shytte is blacke, beset with many a worm,
Soon shall the Shytter come to Grievous Harm!"

And to be honest, in that dismal place I could believe it, although I am surprised we didn't all go down with hysterical constipation - must have been all those lentils. I have no idea where the text came from, as the housemate was very widely read, but I could ask him and see if he remembers."

REFERENCES

Sheffield's Hospitals. © Sheffield Libraries Archives and Information, 2008-2016 (v.1.3)

Stephenson, J. The History of Walkley House Medical Centre. Pickards. 2014.

http://www.ox.ac.uk/news/science-blog/penicillin-oxford-story Accessed 5.6.19

Chapter 1 - Very Inventive Victorians.

PASTEUR and KOCH
THE GERM THEORY OF DISEASE – What Lives Inside

The idea that diseases were caused by germs, micro-organisms, was first recognised by a Dutch scientist, Antoni van Leeuwenhoek, on constructing his first simple microscope in 1677. He decided to use it to examine some water and was amazed to see tiny moving things which he called Animalcules ('little animals').

However, it was a long time until the French chemist Louis Pasteur (1822 – 1895) developed his Germ Theory in 1864. This has become central to our understanding of disease. Using his microscope, Pasteur found that liquids such as beer and milk went 'off' because of the rapid multiplication of very small organisms - germs - in those liquids. He investigated further and found that many of these micro-organisms could be killed by heating the liquid - a preservation method which is called 'pasteurisation'.

Pasteur's extensive work made a significant contribution to the development of the first chemicals developed to attack specific germs - Antibiotics. Pasteur discovered the anthrax bacillus in 1876, at almost exactly the same time as did Robert Koch.

Robert Koch (1843 – 1910) was awarded a Nobel Prize in 1905 for his work developing specific 'chemicals' which targeted germs which caused diseases. His work was partly based on that of Pasteur. He developed tests to prove that a certain germ, like anthrax, was the cause of the disease and gradually this dispelled the longstanding myth that disease was caused by 'bad air'.

Once again, it took many years for antibiotics to be developed, but the work of Pasteur and Koch provided the starting blocks for future scientists.

REFERENCES

Halliday, S. The Great Filth – disease, death and the Victorian city. The History Press 2011. ISBN 978 0 7524 6175 5.

Germ Theory - Science Museum-broughttolife.sciencemuseum.org.uk/broughttolife/techniques/germtheory Accessed 20.2.19

https://wellcomelibrary.org/item/b28036165#?c=0&m=0&s=0&cv=0

Accessed 20.2.19

Chapter 2 - Very Inventive Victorians.

JOSEPH PAXTON (1803 – 1865) – The Giant of Gardeners

Chatsworth House in Derbyshire has been the seat of the Cavendish family since 1552. It was built for Elizabeth née Hardwick, better known today as Bess of Hardwick, when she married Sir William Cavendish. Little detail is known about the early house and gardens, but their 'water feature' was the nearby river Derwent which flowed past the western front of the house. In later years, its water was the solution for a magnificent garden including a water cascade with twenty-four steps, ornamental water features and the Emperor Fountain.

Lancelot 'Capability' Brown, perhaps the most famous English landscape designer, played a large part in Chatsworth's garden development between 1760 and 1764, replacing the formal walled gardens around the house with rolling lawns and beautiful parkland views through the trees. He even altered the course of the river Derwent making it more serpentine in order to look natural and attractive.

At the request of the 6th Duke of Devonshire, Joseph Paxton became Head Gardener at Chatsworth in 1826. He was most famous for the construction, between 1836 and 1840 of his magnificent conservatory with an intricate heating system.

The conservatory was the largest glass building in England before the erection of Paxton's subsequent masterpiece, Crystal Palace in London in 1851. It housed a beautiful tropical garden and so required heating. He needed eight underground boilers fuelled by coal which was transported there by a small underground railway, part of which can still be seen today. A seven-mile network of six-inch hot water pipes provided the heat under the conservatory, fed by steam from the boilers whose fumes were conducted to a chimney in the woods behind. Unfortunately, during WW1, there was no coal and no gardeners and so the plants died and the structure crumbled. It was pulled down in 1920 leaving the base walls to show its extent.

In 1843 Paxton designed and built the Emperor Fountain, fed from a hand dug eight-acre lake 350 feet (110metres) up on the hill above, to give natural water pressure. The fountain was 296 feet (90 metres) high at its maximum height. This made it the world's highest fountain of the time. It was built in honour of the Tsar Nicholas I of Russia who was going to visit but unfortunately never did.

EARLY ELECTRICITY

The water power from the Emperor Lake was subsequently not wasted. It was used to generate Chatsworth's electricity from 1893 to 1936. This made Chatsworth one of England's earliest remote private residences to have electric lighting. The house was then connected to mains electricity and a new turbine installed in 1988 which produced a third of the electricity needed.

In 2013, Chatsworth opened its Renewable Energy Centre, a combined heat and power generation system from a gasification plant using Chatsworth wood chippings. It supplies 97% of the electricity and 72% of the heating for the 300-room house, garden, shops and restaurants.

Flood defence overflow system connected to the Emperor Lake, 2018.

REFERENCES

Halliday, S. Water – a turbulent history 2004. Sutton Publishing Ltd.

ISBN 0-7509-3300-3

https://www.chatsworth.org/art-archives/devonshire-collection/archives/letters-from-joseph-paxton/ Accessed 24.5.19

https://historicengland.org.uk/listing/the-list/list-entry/1000355 Accessed 24.5.19

Chatsworth House Trust Annual Review 2018.

Chapter 3 - Very Inventive Victorians.

FLORENCE NIGHTINGALE (1820 – 1910)
Now Wash Your Hands

Florence Nightingale, known as 'The Lady with the Lamp', developed a 'sanitary concept' whilst working as a military nurse during the Crimean War in 1854. She was very forward-thinking and many of her theories underpin modern Nursing today. Cleanliness was embodied in the Health and Social Care Act of 2008 and subsequent revisions. In every hospital and NHS institution there are instructions about correct hand washing near every basin. The Care Quality Commission takes care to assess whether staff adhere to the principles of cleanliness.

Nightingale's three concepts concerning water and cleanliness were

- Pure water- "well water of a very impure kind is used for domestic purposes. And when epidemic disease shows itself, persons using such water are almost sure to suffer."

- Effective drainage- "all the while the sewer maybe nothing but a laboratory from which epidemic disease and ill health is being installed into the house."

- Cleanliness- "the greater part of nursing consists in preserving cleanliness."

Nightingale had experienced caring for men with war wounds and knew that cleanliness helped them to heal. Nurses' handwashing literally saved lives. She also had a great deal of insight into cleanliness of water, seemingly before the Authorities had accepted the principles.

Ewer and Basin, Chatsworth House

WATER BABIES -
WOE BETIDE YOU

Charles Kingsley's 'The water Babies', published in 1863, built on the theme of cleanliness both physically and spiritually. It described the moral and physical cleansing power of water. It was a didactic moral fable, illustrating how a physically and ethically deprived childhood could cause a poverty of life. It held the Victorian principle that one needed to realise how to improve and work out one's own redemption. ('Those that wish to be clean, clean they will be'). The story of child and teacher is based on the Golden Rule, which was the principle of treating others as oneself would wish to be treated (hence the name of one of the teachers, 'Mrs Doasyouwouldbedoneby').

Water was central to the themes of Victorian cleanliness in all senses, including the Christian thoughts on washing away sins. This story was of a dirty poor child chimney sweep being transformed by living in a watery world as a 'water baby' for a while, into a happy well-adjusted adult as a result, clean inside and out.

Marble bath, Chatsworth House

REFERENCES

https://pmj.bmj.com/content/77/914/802 Accessed 10.1.19

The Health and Social Care Act 2008 Code of Practice on the prevention and control of infections and related guidance. Department of Health. Revised July 2015.

The Water Babies Charles Kingsley. First published in its entirety, in London, 1863.

Chapter 4 - Very Inventive Victorians.

THOMAS HAWKSLEY (1807 – 1893)
The Man Who Turned on the Taps

Thomas Hawksley from Nottingham made clean water available to all and so helped to eradicate cholera from the town. He invented the screw-down tap, in order to address the problems of leaks and drips, and to allow a service twenty- four hours a day to rich and poor alike.

In 1830, when he was only 23, Hawksley constructed a new pumping station for the Trent Waterworks Company, inventing the sand bed idea for water filtration from river water into a collecting reservoir.

In 1831, he was the first engineer to apply the principle of permanent water supply under pressure to this large industrial town. It was under pressure because this supply reservoir was on top of a hill. His system of constant supply meant that anyone could have water whenever they needed it from taps in streets and courtyards. It meant that water could be at constant high pressure which prevented any contamination entering the mains.

Prior to this all water used in Nottingham was taken from shallow wells or directly from rivers and had to be obtained and carried from street pumps. Just over a decade later, between 1848 and 1849, thousands of people in towns throughout Britain died as another cholera epidemic swept the country. However Nottingham, despite its notoriously squalid housing conditions, was relatively unscathed due to Hawksley's clean tap arrangement.

His system could be adapted for hosing streets, putting out fires, filling steam engines, public baths and wash-houses, and watering market gardens. He also advised on the use of sewage as liquid manure, rather than it being discharged straight into rivers.

Thomas Hawksley's ideas and inventions were put to use all over the world. He died in 1893, having been honoured for his contribution to clean safe water supplies, many people benefitting from his philanthropic fount of knowledge.

Chapter 5 - Very Inventive Victorians.

THOMAS CRAPPER (1836 – 1910) - The Saving Flush

Thomas Crapper is credited with providing humanity with a humble yet essential and ingenious device – the modern toilet cistern. Toilets could then be flushed quickly and easily with minimal waste of water.

He was born in the town of Thorne in Yorkshire in 1837, the year of Queen Victoria's accession. He was one of five sons in a family of hardworking people but poor means.

At the tender age of 11 he decided to search for his life's work, whatever that may be, and set off to walk all the 165 miles to London. There he became a Plumber's apprentice.

Queen Victoria's toilet, Westminster Abbey. Not open to the public. Accessed as JLS was giving an organ recital there that day.

Photos: All 3 images on this page taken by J L Stephenson, 2019 with grateful thanks

He had certainly shown his fortitude and tenacity by getting there under his own steam in the first place! So in 1848 he worked with a Master Plumber in Robert Street, Chelsea. He lived in the attic of the works and earned only four shillings a week. He got chillblains, chapped hands and colds.

In midwinter he was allowed to take a hot oven-warmed brick to bed, wrapped in an old towel, to stave off the night chills. He worked a 64-hour week but rapidly learned the knowledge required to fit him for a future career for which he will always be remembered.

Chelsea soon became populated with the rich and famous, not to mention Royalty as well. They had large fine houses with sanitary systems which often broke down, so young Thomas soon became known for his prompt and pleasant attention.

In 1861 he set up business on his own in nearby Marlborough Road as a 'Sanitary Engineer'. His enterprise was assisted by the passing of the Metropolis Water Act in 1872, which put London's water under one authority. Up till then, it had been in the hands of eight separate water companies, each having its own set of regulations. This confused plumbers and engineers who had to abide by each and every one, depending on the area in which they were working. One authority meant one set of water rules.

In those days, the toilet did have a flush from a cistern (tank) above, but it had one valve at the outflow, which often became leaky. Pulling the chain just let out all the water in one go. Some Victorians were quite fastidious and tied the chain down so that the toilet was flushing continuously. This was why London began to run out of water!

Crapper thought about this and realised that prevention of waste was paramount to the success of London's water infrastructure. The 'water closet' always held water in order to prevent sewer gases escaping into the home but the flushing was the problem. He developed the 'Water Waste Preventer' cistern which had no valves and only one moveable part.

This was a no-leak system which was activated by pulling the chain, releasing the water inside the drum (on left of diagram) over the top into the central pipe, from where it flowed down. Then it stopped, and the float (on right of diagram) went down as the water volume fell, and this allowed water to refill the cistern until the float became level again. Then it stopped, and so did a major part of London's water waste.

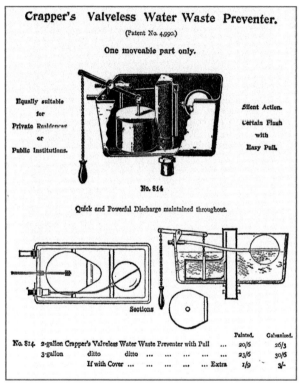

Crapper's Valveless Water Waste Preventer, diagram from Flushed with Pride, 1969. Acknowledgement to Crapper Catalogues

Crapper checked and re-checked his invention. He had a 'test panel' of five toilets in his works, flushed by a 200 gallon water tank on the roof. He perfected the flushing action by trial and error, painstakingly adjusting the mechanism until he was satisfied. He had designed some magnificent china toilet bowls, some decorated with flowers and scrolls with matching chain-pulls.

Crapper ran the risk like all plumbers and water engineers of waterborne disease such as typhoid and cholera, E. coli infection and leptospirosis. However, he caught none of these, but nearly died of smallpox in 1887, and was nursed back to health by his wife.

He traded under the name of 'T. Crapper and Company, Chelsea. Sanitary Engineers to His Majesty' (Edward VII). He was awarded no fewer than four Royal Warrants over a period of half a century. He died in 1910 after serving the Nation and its Royalty in an unforgettable way.

REFERENCE

Reyburn, Wallace. Flushed with pride. The Story of Thomas Crapper. 1969. Macdonald and Company (Publishers) Ltd. London. SBN 356 02995 6.

Chapter 6 - Very Inventive Victorians.

JOSEPH BAZALGETTE (1819 – 1891) –
What Lies Underneath

LIFESAVING LAWS

In 1848, following another severe outbreak of cholera in London, the Public Health Act was the first step on the road to improving peoples' health. It was championed by Edwin Chadwick, a tireless social reformer who had been one of the architects of the Poor Law in 1834. This had made him aware of general sanitation standards amongst the poor, his thinking being that improved conditions may benefit their health and their productivity. He also believed that removing 'filth' (human excrement) would be pivotal in this, separating it from drinking water supplies. This brought him into alignment with John Snow's thinking (see chapter 2 of Section 3).

Bazalgette Water Sewer cover, seen at Blackfriars, London in 2018.

The problems of the Broad Street pump led directly to a change in the sewer system. In the same year as John Snow's thesis was published, 1855, the Metropolis Management Act was passed. Gone were the days of small well and individual water supplies of varying quality, with cesspools for collecting waste. A single connected sewer system under central responsibility came to take its place.

In this way the modern world's first citywide underground water-based sewerage system came into being.

Joseph Bazalgette at that time was Chief Engineer at the Metropolitan Board of Works. He and his team then had a tide of a task ahead of them. Painstaking surveying and sorting, designing and digging, hopefully would bring about a system which collected and discharged the waste into the Thames at as distant a point as possible. Plans were in place but funding was slow to flow. However, Victorian London was soon to discover a greater problem arising from this indecision.

THE THAMES
A STINKING SEWER

The 'Great Stink' descended upon London in the hot summer of 1858 as the waste from two million people sailed past the Houses of Parliament. As a result, the Government quickly authorised money to be used for cleaning up the Thames, raising taxes in order to pay for it. At the same time steam engines and powerful pumps were being developed in order to achieve the improvement in movement of mire. Later, it became obvious that sewage had to be treated before being discharged into rivers.

Bazalgette was therefore committed to developing a centralised sewerage system. This entailed connecting all the various private and public sewers previously constructed by the separate Metropolitan Sewer Boards before 1848. This was an immense undertaking as it involved channeling the waste through miles of underground brick-lined oval tunnels (rather than narrow pipes) into a series of main intercepting sewers which slowly transported it far enough eastwards so that it could be pumped into the Thames - from where it would be swept out to sea.

The point of all this was in fact to rid the inner city of smells (which people still thought transmitted disease). Therefore, the threat of cholera and other waterborne diseases was much reduced but based on the wrong reason.

Bazalgette faced several challenges. Due to the Thames being tidal the water discharge from the new sewers ebbed and flowed, sometimes resulting in dirty water pushing back up and contaminating the intake of drinking water higher up the river. He was to think of another solution.

A further disaster then befell London, as a wake-up call to the problems of sewage in the Thames. In 1878 the pleasure boat Princess Alice sank on the river. About 640 passengers died, many poisoned rather than drowned. This was because the boat went down close to one of the main sewage discharges. This horrified the public as well as the authorities, heightening the awareness of the need for riverside sewage treatment plants. This was duly addressed by Bazalgette who turned his mind to the topic of water treatment.

BRILLIANT BAZALGETTE

The reason for Bazalgette's system lasting so long was that his tunnel system was able to cope with ever-increasing volumes as London expanded. The connections were constructed in such a way that clogging up was avoided. This huge operation was completed in 1865 and officially opened at the Crossness pumping station by HRH The Prince of Wales (later King Edward VII) on 4th April 1865.

Bazalgette then had to consider the banks of the Thames. They were marshy and squelchy, and in the north, as well as being a field of 'filth' it was also home to mosquitos, which transmitted malaria. In Victorian times doctors had seen people with the 'Ague' or 'intermittent fever' which could be treated with quinine. It was in fact malaria and identified as such by Dr Ronald Ross in 1897, who proved the link with mosquitos.

Bazalgette then designed and engineered this north embankment to house the sewerage and treatment system. Now raw, untreated sewage was not dumped in the river. The North embankment was not completed until 1875. It also had to accommodate the Metropolitan District Railways' inner Circle (underground) line and get rid of the mudbanks. The Albert and Victoria Embankments also were rebuilt, using the reclaimed ground for riverside roads and gardens. This reclaimed 52 acres from the Thames and housed more low-level sewers. Bazalgette then turned his engineering skills to design and build several of London's bridges. The ones at Putney, Hammersmith and Battersea are examples.

It can be said that Bazalgette did more for the health of Londoners in the mid-19th century than anyone before or since.

Bazalgette's example sewer system was emulated in other cities the world over. Other cities had begun to struggle with the sewage situation. On a visit to Cambridge, Queen Victoria was admiring the view of Magdalen College from the bridge, when she enquired of her guide about the little bits of paper seen floating in the river (which was toilet paper). Thinking quickly, he told her that they were reminders not to swim in the river!

REFERENCES

Halliday, S. The Great Stink of London: Sir Joseph Bazalgette and the Cleansing of the Victorian Metropolis (Stroud, England, Sutton Publishing Limited, 1999)

https://www.parliament.uk/about/living-heritage/transformingsociety/towncountry/towns/tyne-and-wear-case-study/about-the-group/public-administration/the-1848-public-health-act/

Accessed 15.1.19.

Halliday, S. Water, a Turbulent History. 2004. Sutton Publishing Limited. ISBN 0-7509-3300-3.

Sharp, L. Reconnecting People and Water – Public Engagement and Sustainable Urban Water management. Earthscan (Routledge) 2017. ISBN 978 0415 72845

Chapter 7 - Very Inventive Victorians.

JOHN BATEMAN (1810 – 1889) The Hundred-Mile Aqueduct

Another example of Victorian endeavour is to be found in the concept and building of a one-hundred-mile aqueduct designed to supply the industries and people of Manchester with clear fresh water from Thirlmere in the Lake District.

In 1874 an engineer John Bateman was called in to invent a way that Manchester, a rapidly growing city with important cotton mills, could be supplied in a sustainable way with clear water. Back in 1869 it had been suggested that a reservoir be built in the Lake District in order to supply London, but the distance was obviously too far, and the North of England needed to be developed.

There was little in the way of public consultation regarding the proposed reservoir. When the news came out there was vociferous and understandable objections to the acquisition of land and this required a Bill in Parliament in order to compulsorily purchase it.

Between 1890 and 1894, based on Bateman's plans, a tall dam was built across the narrowest part of the valley, and in a fairly short time St John's Beck filled it with water. A magnificent aqueduct was built from this reservoir all the way to the Audenshaw reservoirs on the east side of Manchester which is 102 miles (163 km) long. It was gravity-fed as the Lake District was hilly and lay at a point higher than Manchester. Therefore no pumps were required to move the water along, just a set of syphons to control water flow into the pipes, and a steady flow of the water at two miles per hour. The water was conducted through pipes across bridges or underground in order to keep up the gentle gradient downwards, and therefore the flow. Thanks to the magnificent engineering, it is still in use today.

Other cities may have required less endeavour in order to obtain water for their industries. Nottingham, for example, was built on an area well supplied by wells and springs, which were clean and clear for use in the famous lace-making.

REFERENCE
Hoyle, N. Sankey, K. Thirlmere Water – a Hundred Miles and a Hundred Years. Centwrite publishers, 1994. ISBN 0-9523413-0-1.

Chapter 1 - Sustaining Supplies.

RESERVOIRS

From where does Sheffield's water come? How does such a clean, clear supply find its way into our homes?

Sheffield's water is mainly from the river Ouse and the river Derwent, only in part being from the reservoirs which we see on the high ground around Sheffield. The water that we source from rivers is typically classed as hard water, because the water gathers minerals (mainly calcium and magnesium) as it runs through and over rocks. Research suggests a protective effect of drinking water hardness against cardiovascular disease (mainly strokes and heart attacks). By contrast, water from reservoirs is normally softer as it comes from high ground and moorlands.

OUR RESERVOIRS

Agden and Dam Flask reservoirs, from Mortimer Road.

Sheffield's reservoirs are part of its beautiful landscape. South Yorkshire has at least fifteen reservoirs, and more minor ones, but not all these serve water to the area. Some reservoirs are 'balancing' or 'service' reservoirs, which receive water pumped or channelled into them, their purpose being to balance supply with demand. Others are 'impounding' reservoirs into which a river flows naturally. Either type can be used for domestic water service, or for topping up rivers when they run low. Water levels in reservoirs are carefully controlled. For example, if a major storm is forecast, water is let out prior and during the storm in order to prevent overfilling of the reservoir and flooding of the river below.

Most modern reservoirs have a specially designed draw-off tower that can draw off water at different levels depending on its quality and the depth of the water in the reservoir, in order to supply the cleanest drinking water.

South Yorkshire is therefore a 'lakeland' with its own particular character. It is being conserved by Sheffield Lakeland Partnership – an active and ecological collaboration managed by Sheffield and Rotherham Wildlife Trust. It works together with Yorkshire Water, Town and City Councils, Natural England, the Environment Agency, South Yorkshire Archaeology Service, community foundations and representatives of landowners and local access groups. Over the coming years the Partnership will involve many more interested and knowledgeable organisations, supported in part by Lottery funding.

Each reservoir has a different tale to tell. From its inception to the modern day, it tells of skill and hardship in design and building; of times of satisfaction and of want in its supply; of disasters, for example, Dale Dyke reservoir (Chapter 3). There is also a different ecosystem around each and different birds and plants to see throughout the seasons. At the time of writing, 2019, there is an active programme of replacing the old pine woods around some reservoirs with sustainable native hardwoods like oak and beech which will afford a greater natural habitat for plants, insects and animals. Each reservoir was designed with a flank of land around it, generally with pine woods. This was in order to keep farm land and other sources of possible contamination away from its shores. There was often a 'New Road' built part way round each reservoir to allow easier access, as well as concessionary footpaths from which we all can benefit. I have run around all fifteen reservoirs at different times of year and enjoyed the different views and wildlife, at the same time admiring the individual characteristics of each expanse of water.

The first reservoir in Sheffield was constructed in 1712, near the White House in Upperthorpe. As the population increased, by 1737 a few more small dams had been built and in 1795 a chain of reservoirs in the Crookesmoor Valley was started. However, by 1830, the town had 90,000 inhabitants and so an Act of Parliament created the Sheffield Water Works Company which was given power to create further reservoirs as needed. Two years later Sheffield suffered a cholera outbreak, making a good supply of clean water imperative.

The Sheffield Water Works Company building, in Barker's Pool area, now a pub/restaurant.

Hadfield Dam at Crookes and the Middle Redmires reservoirs were the first of Sheffield's new reservoirs to be built. By 1845 the population had risen to 120,000 and a further Act enabled two more reservoirs to be built at Redmires, along with two compensation dams in the Rivelin Valley. Sheffield's industry continued to thrive, bringing the population to 150,000 by 1854. Another Act brought into existence two reservoirs in Bradfield Dale, one on the river Agden and a compensation reservoir in the Loxley Valley.

REDMIRES RESERVOIRS

The Upper, Middle and Lower Redmires reservoirs form a group of three on the south west side of Sheffield. They are fed from streams from the Hallam Moor. They were built to provide clean drinking water via a water course which passed through Lodge Moor, into Fulwood at the top of the hill, down to a small collection reservoir at Carsick Hill ('sick' being from an old name 'sitch' meaning 'stream'), then distributed further down the hill to dwellings, all gravity-fed.

Redmires Lower & spillway. February 2019

It is a splendid water course, lined by dressed stone and partly underground. A walker can trace its track from Redmires to Carsick, though some is underground at the top of Slayleigh Lane.

A pump house, channels and waterways leading from the Redmires reservoirs.

Here is a photograph of part of the curved channel built to collect water from surrounding moorland, to drain into Redmires lower reservoir. In summer this channel is often dry.

At the time of building the Redmires reservoirs local farmers saw a development opportunity and opened their homes as public houses to offer beer to thirsty workmen. The stone sign of one of them, the Trout and Partridge, can be seen today by the road up to the lower reservoir. This one offered food as well, and bore the inscription 'ICH DIEN DINNER', a mixture of old German and English. The 'ich dien' means 'I serve,' as

written under the well-known Prince of Wales feathers, and 'dinner' referred to the offering of food as well as ale. The words can just be made out under the three fish.

The Upper reservoir was drained in 2018 to allow reconstruction of its dam wall, replacing the clay and shale with iron piling. A remarkable piece of history emerged in the centre of the reservoir linking 2018 with Sheffield's important industrial past.

Jan 2019: Upper Redmires, drained. Dam reconstruction.

The Long Causeway was an important road. The trail was laid in Roman times, running west from Sheffield town up to Redmires. From there it led to the Hope Valley via Stanage and beyond via the Winnats Pass. It was a packhorse track and most of it was paved with flagstones, enabling the passage of goods from Sheffield and for the important traffic of salt back from Cheshire.

The milestone is made of red sandstone typical of the area (hence 'Red'mires) and indicates that the route lay along this way, Sheffield being 16 miles from Brough (Derbyshire) further along. This stone is normally under water when the upper reservoir is full.

A small subterranean service reservoir, Rudd Hill, can be seen in the photograph on page 27. Before distribution it receives water from the Redmires reservoirs and can be seen here being tested by a water engineer.

The Redmires water treatment works (WTW) was built in 1950, being located by the Lower reservoir where preliminary treatment took place, using lime in order to separate the natural aluminium from the water. A new WTW was installed in 1988 using the Sirofloc process, the first use of this in an operational water-treatment works outside Australia. This employed magnetised iron oxide, magnetite, to draw away the impurities from drinking water and did not require a filter. Eventually it was closed in 1997 as larger WTW plants took over elsewhere.

DAMFLASK RESERVOIR, LOXLEY VALLEY

Damflask reservoir.

Damflask reservoir in the Bradfield area, was built by the Sheffield Water Company and completed in 1896 with the dam walls being constructed from local stone. The village of Damflask was nestled in the valley a little further along from Dale Dyke reservoir, and was made up of a few houses, a corn mill, paper mill, wire mill and a pub. It was victim to the Dale Dyke flood in 1864 and was never rebuilt. Instead, another reservoir was sited there, taking its name.

Its original purpose was as a compensation reservoir to ensure a continuous flow of water to the River Loxley downstream and therefore to supply both fresh drinking water and reliable running water to the population and industries of Sheffield.

In August 2002 Yorkshire Water opened all the area to public access under the Countryside and Rights of Way Act 2000. In 2015 it brought up the path around it to a high standard to allow disabled access as well, together with information boards. The walk around the reservoir is 3.8 miles. The village of Low Bradfield lies at the upper end where there was a mill before it was severely damaged in the Dale Dyke flood (1864). The reservoir also is home to sailing clubs and training, as well as available for fishing (roach, pike and perch).

Fly Agaric, (poisonous) as seen on the banks of Damflask in 2018, September.

A Mandarin duck, as seen on Damflask in 2018, June.

The river Loxley runs from Damflask down the Loxley Valley and the very pleasant walk alongside it takes us past the remains of old industries such as Wragg's brickworks and previous (and current) water treatment plants. Wildlife is living happily beside the ruins. I saw this Dipper at the edge of the river.

A Dipper. Seen by the Loxley River, March 2018.

The old water treatment plant at Low Bradfield awaits its destiny which is uncertain at present. It was built in 1913 and extended in 1953, in order to filter water from Agden, Dale Dyke and Strines reservoirs. In 1930 the Filter House was the first building in the village to have a telephone installed. The treatment plant closed in 1995 as a larger new modern plant was opened in the Loxley Valley.

Low Bradfield old water treatment plant and tanks

In 2019 work was completed to improve the spillways of Damflask in order to allow greater run-off in times of high water levels. This could happen increasingly often due to climate change and  sudden torrential rains. At time of writing, August 2019, the small Derbyshire town of Whaley Bridge was threatened with the bursting of the earth embankment dam of Toddbrook reservoir above it and the population was evacuated.

AGDEN RESERVOIR

Agden reservoir was completed in 1869. It was built to collect water from nearby moorland as were reservoirs Dale Dyke and Strines. It is mostly surrounded by pine forest and has Agden Bog, a protected wetland, on the north side. There are the remains of three ruined farmhouses and what was a reservoir keeper's cottage (now a private dwelling). It is an impounding reservoir. Care needs to be taken when walking on its sometimes wet pathways and steep sides.

Above:
Agden reservoir in summer
Below previous column:
In the evening.

DALE DYKE RESERVOIR – BRADFIELD DALE

Dale Dyke reservoir was built in 1860 to supply drinking water to an exponentially expanding Sheffield and to power mills. Only four years later it caused a great tragedy.

View of Dale Dyke

The Lower Bradfield Reservoir as it was also known, was built to hold over seven hundred million gallons of water and covered 78 acres. It is 700 feet above sea level. Its waters are dark and sides very steep under the surface, and it is bordered mainly by woodland. There is a valve house to be found here (not now used), and a current pump and inflow control, the original arch being dated 1878.

The breaching of the dam wall in 1864 caused one of the largest man-made disasters in British history. The Great Sheffield Flood, as it became known, inflicted massive damage downstream along the rivers Loxley and Don, and through the centre of Sheffield. Around 250 people lost their lives. The reservoir was rebuilt in 1875 on a smaller scale. One can see the line of the original dam which is indicated by a marker stone. A flood memorial was erected in 1991 by Bradfield Historical Society to commemorate those who drowned.

A sprig of Larch, as seen next to Dale Dyke.

STRINES RESERVOIR – BRADFIELD DALE

The reservoir was constructed in 1869 following the Dale Dyke disaster. It collected water for the growing Sheffield from surrounding moorland, as did the other two nearby. Sheffield had previously received its water supply from the Crookesmoor dams close to the town centre but by the mid-19th century these were becoming inadequate.

Strines Reservoir is the smallest of the Bradfield Dale reservoirs and there is no circular walk around it.

Above: Strines reservoir in February and right in June 2018 from a different perspective.

RIVELIN RESERVOIRS

The Upper and Lower Rivelin Dams (the Lower being completed in 1845 and the Upper in 1848) are a pair of water storage reservoirs situated in the Rivelin Valley, 5 miles (8 km) west of Sheffield along the Rivelin Valley Road. This road was built on water company land in 1907 between Malin Bridge and Rivelin Mill Bridge to connect with the main Sheffield to Manchester road, now the A57. It is lined by lime trees along its length of three and a half miles.

The dams are owned by Yorkshire Water and provide drinking water to 319,000 people, as well as compensation water for the River

Rivelin. The dams receive water from both the river Rivelin, and from the Derwent Valley via Ladybower Reservoir, the latter via the Rivelin Tunnel which runs eastwards from Ladybower to the Lower Rivelin Dam. This tunnel, four and a half miles long, was built between 1903 and 1909 and uses the plentiful supplies of the river Derwent as compensation water for the river Rivelin.

From top to bottom: Part of Rivelin Lower dam.
View in winter.
The new treatment plant being built 2017-18.
A spillway in use.

The river Rivelin rises on the Hallam moors, in north west Sheffield, and joins the river Loxley at Malin Bridge. The river flows through the Rivelin Valley which affords many interesting walks through the woods on the Nature Trail there.

The Rivelin is a relatively fast-flowing river, fed by the water from the moorland peat. It drops 80 metres between Rivelin Mill Bridge and Malin Bridge. Since Roman times its strong flow provided the power source for water wheels – twenty in total, belonging to twenty mills over the centuries. Each had its artificially created ponds, some of which can still be seen today as they have been preserved by the Rivelin Valley Conservation Group. The wheels were part of cutlery and metal-working industries, forges and flour mills. To channel the water there are walls to create mill races.

Oak in autumn
Dog rose.
Both as seen in the woods
around Rivelin Valley.

RIVELIN WATER TREATMENT WORKS

The Works, housed in elegant stone-built housings, stand below the dam wall of the Lower Reservoir. They were constructed in 1913 and pumped 7.5 million gallons per day of treated Rivelin water to the Hadfield service reservoir at Crookesmoor. This daily flow increased to 12 million gallons in 1946 with further improvements in the technology. The works also pump Rivelin water uphill to Redmires.

The water treatment plant was updated and extended in 1992. It used the Sirofloc process, as the one at Redmires did, in order to remove impurities from the water, employing magnetic iron filings. At the completion of the refurbishment there was an Open Day for the public to view the new buildings and process. This engaged them in general understanding and admiration of where clean domestic water comes from, and increased awareness of the public's responsibility in the use of water.

A turbine at the inlet of the works was added in 2008 to generate renewable energy. This was then used at the works.

Early 2018 saw the completion of a £24 million scheme to improve the drinking water at Rivelin by upgrading the treatment works. An underground building has been constructed to house new clarifying settlement tanks which supply the first phase of the water treatment process.

LADYBOWER RESERVOIR

This well-known reservoir forms a Y-shaped expanse of water along with two other reservoirs, Derwent reservoir and Howden reservoir. The river Ashop flows into the reservoir from the west, the river Derwent flows south initially through Howden then through Derwent reservoirs, and finally through Ladybower, joining the Ladybower Brook in doing so.

Ladybower reservoir, the two parts as seen from Win Hill at relatively low water level.

Ladybower was built between 1935 and 1943 by the Derwent Valley Water Board to boost water supplies to the East Midlands from the other two reservoirs. The original workers' houses remain on its west bank today as does the low stone building which housed the water treatment plant.

It was thought that the reservoir would take at least three years to fill, but actually it took under two years as the river flow was high.

Sloe (Blackthorn) with lichen, seen next to Ladybower in the autumn

Below: The old WTW, now housing

The dam differs from Howden and Derwent reservoirs in that it is a clay-cored earth embankment and not a solid masonry dam. Below this embankment is a trench 180 feet (55 m) deep and 6 feet (1.8 m) wide filled with concrete, stretching 500 feet (150 m) into the hills each side, to stop water leaking round the dam. Two viaduct bridges, Ashopton and Ladybower, were built to carry the trunk roads over the reservoir. Despite the outbreak of WW2 and the shortage of workforce and materials, the project went ahead due to the strategic importance of maintaining supplies. Ladybower was finally opened in 1945 by King George VI.

Fear of flooding caused the Ladybower dam wall to be raised and strengthened during the 1990s. Materials were brought to the site on the Derwent Valley Water Board's own branch railway line and their sidings off the main line in the Hope Valley.

Two famous features of Ladybower are its bell mouth spillways at the end nearest the dam wall. Each are beautifully built in stone and are 80 feet (24m) wide. Each discharges via its own valve house down the hill at the base of the dam.

Views of Viaduct: Ashopton viaduct and Ladybower Reservoir. Boats on one side (upper); tranquil picnic beside Ladybower on the other (bottom).

Bell mouthed spillways by the dam in Ladybower reservoir, at low water (top, July 2017) and high water (below, January 2018).

The water from Ladybower is used for river control and to compensate for the water held by all three dams, along with supply into the drinking water system and hydroelectricity

generation. The drinking water is pumped (rather than using gravity) to be treated at Bamford water treatment works by Severn Trent Water. Treated water flows south down the 28 miles (45 km) long Derwent Valley aqueduct to a covered service reservoir at Ambergate. From there it supplies clean water to the cities of Nottingham, Derby and Leicester. The aqueduct passes through the park of Chatsworth House. The path of the aqueduct is marked by a series of valve houses built of stone and domed steel access chambers. A tunnel carries some of the water from the Derwent Valley eastwards through the hill and into the lower of the two Rivelin dams to supply Sheffield.

FLOODED VILLAGES UNDER LADYBOWER

The villages of Ashopton (near the viaduct bearing its name) and of Derwent were flooded as Ladybower was built. The houses of Ashopton were demolished before the flooding commenced.

The village of Ashopton in 1935 about to be flooded, with the looming viaduct in the background. With permission: www.picturesheffield.com and Sheffield Archives and Local Studies Library

A little further up the valley Derwent was fairly intact and the structure was revealed in a dry summer fourteen years later in 1949. The packhorse bridge over the river Derwent was taken down and rebuilt at the top of Howden reservoir. The spire of the church had not been demolished and it was visible above water level until 1947. People swam out to it and as it was considered a hazard it was destroyed.

There have been dry summers in 1976, 1995 and again in 2018, when some village remains have been seen, but little is left now. In 2018 people tried to investigate the few stones remaining, but one person got stuck in the mud and had to be rescued. Some unfortunately left graffiti.

Low water levels at Derwent summer 2018, showing people exploring the area and the old pump house

The spire of Derwent church before its demolition. With permission: www.picturesheffield.com and Sheffield Archives and Local Studies Library

DERWENT RESERVOIR

Derwent reservoir lies between Ladybower and Howden reservoirs. It affords a beautiful walk along its banks connecting with ancient walking paths over the moors. There is a Visitor centre nearby.

Derwent Dam, water inflow

View across Derwent Dam through archway

Painting: Water Wagtail as seen next to Derwent reservoir.

Water flowing over Derwent Dam

Derwent and Howden were built before Ladybower between 1901 and 1916. Construction of the neo-Gothic solid masonry dam began in 1902, a year after the building of Howden dam commenced. It proved a daunting task. The huge dressed stones (with a patterned surface) that formed the walls of the dam were carried along a specially created railway from the quarries at Bole Hill near Grindleford. Over a thousand workers from all over the UK lived in a specially constructed self-contained town called Birchinlee (named from a nearby farmhouse which it replaced) or "Tin Town", referring to the corrugated tin from which the houses were built.

The flow from Derwent reservoir was found to be insufficient for the population in 1916, so between 1920 and 1931 the rivers Alport and Ashop were diverted into it through tunnels.

The forestry around the Upper Derwent reservoirs has typically been pine, planted to stabilise the banks and provide shelter. In 2006 the Upper Derwent Valley Woodlands' Conservation Management Plan suggested a more sustainable mix of native trees like oak and birch, which could form a greater habitat for wildlife while still maintaining the banks.

Trees around the Upper Derwent Valley.

Derwent reservoir is perhaps most famous for its part played as a practice area for the bombers of the second World War.

THE DAMBUSTERS

In 1943 the RAF 617 Squadron used Derwent to practice low level flying in preparation for the Dam Buster raids on the Ruhr Valley dams in Germany. Lancaster bombers were flown at night to a height of only 60ft, focussing their two spotlight beams together in order to maintain this distance above the water level. A specially created bomb, the 'Bouncing Bomb', was designed to skim over the water before sinking and exploding at the base of the dam. (This latter exercise was not practised at Derwent).

HOWDEN RESERVOIR

This reservoir lies above Derwent, its western half being in Derbyshire and its eastern half in South Yorkshire. Its history is recounted above.

View of Howden Dam.

There is a 28m (92ft) difference in height between Howden and Derwent reservoirs. This has been used to generate electricity within Howden dam using diesel generators but these are not environmentally sustainable. Severn Trent Water has therefore, in partnership with MWH (a global water firm), built the Howden Hydro-Power Scheme. A 'cross flow' turbine generates electricity from the water fall down an abandoned pipe leading from Howden to Bamford Water Treatment Works. It is enough to power 425 UK homes each year.

BROOMHEAD AND MOREHALL RESERVOIRS

Broomhead and Morehall reservoirs lie end to end in the Ewden Valley near Stocksbridge. They were opened in 1929 by Sheffield Corporation. The workers building the site lived in a specially-constructed community – Ewden Village. These reservoirs were constructed to receive water drainage from more than thirty-seven thousand acres of moorland.

Broomhead Dam and valve house on a misty autumn day

Pine cone and lichen-covered twig as seen on the walks round Broomhead and Morehall. The presence of lichen indicates low air pollution levels. I found three types of lichen on this twig.

UNDERBANK AND MIDHOPESTONES RESERVOIRS

The water from Midhope reservoir goes to Barnsley (it was built by Barnsley Water corporation) and Underbank is a small supply reservoir nearby

Midhopestones Reservoir

Underbank Reservoir

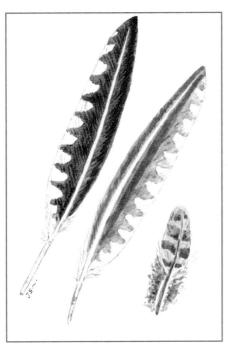

Curlew feathers as seen on the moors around Midhope reservoir.

LANGSETT RESERVOIR

Langsett was one of the first reservoirs. It constructed between 1898 and 1904 and is fed by the Little Don (or Porter) river. It is around a mile long, and supplies water for Sheffield and Barnsley via the Langsett Treatment Works. It is the largest of the water supply reservoirs in the Sheffield area. Its catchment area covering over 5,000 acres is the Langsett Moors to the west. It is home to a rich variety of wildlife and plants.

The embankment is one of the largest of its kind in the UK. Langsett woods around the reservoir were planted in 1962, comprising twenty five hectares of coniferous woodland. With the support of the RSPB and the Forestry Commission, the woodland is being reconstructed to make better habitats for native birds such as woodpeckers and warblers. Oak and Birch will replace the pines, and woody shrubs like rowan (overleaf), blackthorn and willow will flourish.

Heathers

Sweet Chestnut and Rowan

The area is used for sheep farming and grouse shooting, as well as providing enjoyable walks with views. It is a haven for birdwatchers and artists. I saw this common sandpiper whilst running round it. Fishermen say that the trout grow larger in the Porter river due to the freshwater crayfish living there.

Langsett Water Treatment Works replace the older ones which used sand filter beds to treat the water, which was safe to drink but brown in colour (from the peat moorland). The new works were completed in 1986 and used a further process to clarify the water. The works are being upgraded again at the present time.

Pheasant Feathers, one down feather and one flight feather, found on Langsett Moor

WARTIME AT LANGSETT

During WW2 around Langsett and Midhope reservoirs there was a tank range used for Army training in 1940. Roads around the moors of Langsett were built from rubble collected from the city of Sheffield after each blitz. An Army camp was built too. They tried out the new British Churchill tank (made in Chapeltown) and remains can still be seen of the targets which were used for practice. One of these was 'North America', an old farmhouse of which a few stones still stand.

The reservoir was protected in wartime by the use of Catenary defences. These were steel cables crossing each reservoir, each cross-cable being 300ft above the water level. From these weighted vertical wires hung at intervals as a barrier to any air attack. The last of the 325ft pylons was only removed in1955.

So our reservoirs each have a fascinating story to tell, contributing to the history of our fresh water supplies.

REFERENCES

https://www.wildsheffield.com/discover/your-community/sheffield-lakeland-landscape-partnership/ Accessed 12.7.19

http://www.bradfield-walkers.org.uk/Walks/Damflask.html Accessed 12.7.19

http://www.bradfield-walkers.org.uk/Walks/UghillMoor.html Accessed 12.7.19

http://www.calmview.eu/SheffieldArchives/CalmView/Record.aspx?src=CalmView.Catalog&id=YWA

J.Edward Vickers. A Popular History of Sheffield. Applebaum Bookshop Ltd, Sheffield. ISBN 9 780906 787045

Howard Smith with Ann Beedham, The Long Causeway. 2017. Witley Press. ISBN 978-1-5272-1830-7

http://www.waterprojectsonline.com/case_studies/2016/Yorkshire_Rivelin_2016.pdf

Stephen Harwood, (September 2000). "Severn Trent Water, The Ladybower Reservoir Dam Refurbishment Scheme" (PDF). Archived from the original (PDF) on 2011-10-04. Retrieved 23.4.19.

Louise Catling, Ibrahim Abubakar, Iain Lake, Louise Swift, Paul Hunter. Final report for contract DWI/70/2/176 Date: 21st October 2005. University of East Anglia and Drinking Water Inspectorate Review of evidence for relationship between incidence of cardiovascular disease and water hardness School of Medicine, Health Policy and Practice 2 School of Environmental Sciences University of East Anglia, Norwich, Norfolk, NR4 7TJ.

Bill Bevan. Town of Tin. British Archaeology Magazine 59, June 2001 (see www.britarch.ac.uk)

Chapter 2 - Sustaining Supplies.

FRIENDLY FOUNTAINS

Liverpool, not London, saw the first ever drinking fountain in Britain.

Liverpool's population was expanding greatly in the early nineteenth century as it was the Northern port for manufacturing and handling goods (cotton, sugar and tobacco). It was a centre for emigrating people to far-flung areas of the British Empire. In 1801 the city had 80,000 inhabitants but by 1841, as recorded in the census, the population had increased to over a quarter of a million people. A burgeoning number of people were required to support the expansion of Victorian business. At that time Liverpool city was the greatest contributor to the Nation's wealth.

This brought with it the added problems of housing and sanitation, and during the working day, subsistence. In the heat and hardship of the dockers' daily toils, their main requirement was a clean plentiful supply of water.

It was Liverpool which pioneered the idea of 'cleansing' the working people by opening the Frederick Street baths in 1842. The bathhouse came out of the concern that general cleansing was required in order to prevent another cholera epidemic such as the one which had hit the city only ten years previously. It became a model of social reform and improvement. This led to the passing of the Baths and Washhouses Acts in 1846 which encouraged other local authorities to follow suit.

Charles Melly was one of the wealthy Victorian businessmen of Liverpool. His father was Swiss so he often travelled back to his boyhood home in Geneva. He had many early memories of Swiss spa and mineral water treatments. Such tourism became increasingly popular, made possible by connections of the new railway system. During his visits he was fascinated that people had access to free clean drinking water at street corners, from impressive fountains – a system set up in Europe centuries earlier by the Romans. On return to Liverpool Melly made enquiries around the dock workers, and found that his idea was met with a positive response. Accordingly, in 1853, he installed two public taps at the docks and assessed their popularity; he was convinced that a public fountain would be appreciated by everyone.

Flowing from that, the first public drinking fountain in Britain was set up in a wall on the Princes Dock at his own expense. After three months an assessment showed that more than two thousand people came to use it in a period of twelve hours.

The first drinking fountain, at Princes Dock, Liverpool. Photo: a kind friend, received with many thanks.

Charles Melly's message was that the basic necessity of life, water, should be free at the point of use and available to all. He was motivated by his Unitarian faith which supported the moral of 'cleanliness and sobriety'.

Melly had managed to convince the local authority of the merits of free drinking water and in only five years there were a total of forty such fountains on the streets of Liverpool. In 1858, he promoted his work widely, and it came to the ears of the government in London.

FOUNTAINS FOR LONDON – SAMUEL GURNEY

A generous gentleman by the name of Samuel Gurney was a banker, an MP and a Quaker in London. He was part of the general social reform taking place in Britain in Victorian times. The idea of Charles Melly's water fountains was especially acceptable to the Quaker movement who approved of 'temperance' – promoting the drinking of natural water in preference to alcohol. He therefore made the quest for free public drinking water his own personal crusade in London although he had several challenges along the way. Finally, in 1859, his idea was accepted and at his own expense a fountain was installed in the railings of St Sepulchre's Church in the City of London, as it happened, located opposite Newgate Prison where his aunt, Elizabeth Fry (née Gurney), had been a radical prison reformer.

The fountain in the railings of St Sepulchre's Church, Holborn, London. Photo: J L Stephenson

It had two drinking cups of brass attached by chains, which are still there today. The reminder is inscribed underneath 'REPLACE THE CUP'. It was widely welcomed, as it came at a time when the water quality of London was poor and cholera was rife. It was so popular that the Association built a further 85 fountains over the next six years.

This first fountain had the inscription 'Filtered water from the New River Company, as the water was drawn from a rural Hertfordshire spring rather than the possibly contaminated wells of London. It was filtered too.

The Metropolitan Free Drinking Fountains Association came into being and set about the task of making free drinking water from fountains available throughout London. These were to be made of granite to keep the water cool and to contain a filter made of animal charcoal. The inevitable difficulty was that of funding them. A small fountain in a wall cost £25 (equivalent to £1,000) and a free-standing one £50 (£2,000). There was no over-arching water company but at that time fifty-four London parishes, each with its own committee in charge of pipes and water, supplied in its own parish. The Association tried by promotion and persuasion but the arguments did not produce fruit, so again, they measured the popularity of the three installed fountains, with between 3,000 and 6,500 people drinking from them in one day. The problem was how to install and run a service free at point of delivery, whose real costs are quite appreciable. It parallels our problems with the NHS funding at the present time.

The different private water suppliers had differing views on whether they should and could afford to pay towards the maintenance and supply to the fountains. Some felt that it encouraged people to take the free water to their homes and store it and so use less of the domestic paid-for water. The fact that householders did this was unsurprising because often the water supply to houses was intermittent and not of high quality. The first fountains ran continuously but the decision was then made to install taps with a certain saving of water; some were turned off over the winter months. It may have been then that the people turned to the public houses to slake their thirst instead.

By the mid-1860's parishes across central London had fountains along the main routes, and in poor districts such as St Giles and Whitechapel they were installed outside workhouses and some pubs.

This was an effort to entice people away from drinking too much beer! In fact, some of the brewers sought fame and social status by donating drinking water.

HISTORY OF SPECIFIC FOUNTAINS

Every fountain tells a story - often one of great endeavour and public spiritedness.

Here is a random selection of fountains near and far which I have come across with a little bit of their salient history.

London – Millbank, Westminster

The Buxton Memorial Fountain (1865)

This beautiful covered fountain was designed by Charles Buxton, MP, and was erected to celebrate the abolition of slavery in 1834. It was restored in 2007. It is made of limestone and granite, with a spectacular enamelled roof in different colours topped by a finial.

In 1866, however, cholera revisited London. 2,661 people died in a week, mainly in the east of the city. This set people thinking about how it was spread and how to prevent it erupting again. By the end of the century it was science rather than social reform which led to improved standards of drinking water and sanitation.

The Association's drinking fountains numbered 690 in 1892. Financially the Association was struggling to fund them. It became clearer to everyone that this very popular free drinking water should be a public service rather than be the donation from a charity. It wasn't until 1902 that the Metropolis Water Act came into being which changed the ownership of London's water supply to a municipal body which included Public Health. Water quality was paramount but this partially solved the problem of funding the fountains.

Bakewell

There stands on the Baslow Road at the intersection with Station Road just before the bridge over the river Wye an elegant Victorian water fountain built of local stone. It now bears a street lamp and the water no longer flows. It was known as 'Cross's Folly' and was erected by a group of generous townsmen led by Robert Cross of Milford House to celebrate the success of the town's new water supply in 1872. This was needed as the population grew, the water being sourced from a reservoir on Coombs Hill and a soft water spring at the Fallinge, rather than piped from wells in Manners Wood as previously.

Bakewell was a town of industrial importance due to its being on a trade route to Buxton (now the A6). It has been a market town since the 13th century and attracted rich benefactors, especially when the routes into Bakewell became turnpike roads in 1759.

Bakewell has had a spa since 1697. A Public Bath was constructed that year by the Duke of Rutland on Bath Street in 1805, together with its Bath Gardens for relaxation. The Bath House was rebuilt in 1829 and was occupied by Mr White Watson, a renowned geologist and botanist, whose fame encouraged visits from plantsmen, historians, industrialists, scientists and geologists The warm spring was ducted underground in the early nineteenth century to form a warm bath, but the spring dried up in the 1930's due to works on the sewers in Bath Street.

SHEFFIELD'S FOUNTAINS

The Old Town Hall in Waingate, central Sheffield, was built in 1807 in order to house the Town Trustees and the Petty and Quarter sessions (law courts). The courtrooms were connected to the nearby Sheffield Police offices by underground passages. The building underwent some restructuring, including addition of the clock tower. A drinking water fountain was built into the wall in Castle Street in 1897.

The fountain will have been used for the passing public on the local busy roads. The building became the Sheffield Crown Court soon after it was added.

The building has been disused since 1997 and awaits future plans for its revival.

The fountain of the Old Town Hall, Sheffield

Broad Lane is graced with a drinking fountain halfway down in the car park opposite the medical centre. It was erected in 1875 to the memory of James Montgomery the journalist and hymn-writer.

The inscription is now illegible. The fountain was obviously well used, as seen by the wearing down of the stone foot rests. There was a Victorian street lamp on the top.

William Jeffcock was the first Lord Mayor of Sheffield, and the man who built High Hazels House (now Tinsley Park Golf Club) in 1850. He was a Justice of the Peace and an officer in the West Riding Yeomanry Cavalry.

A fountain and water trough dedicated to him can be found at the top of Richmond Road. He died in Ireland in 1871 and is buried in Handsworth churchyard.

Meersbrook Park Fountain

Meersbrook Park with Sheffield beyond.

This elegant granite fountain is dated 1889 and was erected by the Society of Oddfellows in memory of William Westran, one of their Founder members. He was the Society's 'corresponding secretary' for 21 years, dying while in office in his 66th year. What a public-spirited tribute this was.

Low Bradfield There is a simple drinking fountain dated 1900, erected near the Parish Hall, given by Miss Mary Smith who lived in the large house next to the bus turning area on Lee Moor Road, Low Bradfield. She had no children, and desired to leave some money in the public interest. This kind donation was the result.

The original fountain had the word 'WATER' inscribed in the centre of the stone above the bowl, but this was removed when the fountain was decommissioned due to the difficulties in ensuring that the water was clean enough to drink.

The remaining inscription 'Mary Ann Smith - God's gift to Man' therefore does not bear its original meaning. It would otherwise have read: "Water-God's gift to Man" under her name.

Midhopestones

This little village 11 miles north of Sheffield is in the valley of the Little Don river between Underbank and Midhope reservoirs. It has an easily-missed item of water history: a tiny but faithful well. At the start of the footpath to Underbank reservoir, the 'Potters' Well' with its stone-flagged pathway can be seen. It dates from 1720 when it was made into water access for Midhopestones pottery. Until 1919 it was the sole source of water for this village.

Youlgreave

Long before the days of Water Companies and mains piping this village near Bakewell had its own central water supply for domestic use of its inhabitants.

Before Youlgreave had its own water works the people got their water from the nearby river Bradford and a number of wells. However, there was a higher death rate of children in the summer months when the river levels were low, due to suspected contamination or infection.

The Friendly Society of Women was founded in 1827, and this Society raised funds for the setting up of a safer village water supply.

Water from a nearby spring was piped to a stone cistern (pictured) holding 1,500 gallons in the village centre at a cost of £252, 13 shillings and 10 pence halfpenny. The cistern refilled overnight and a Water Keeper was paid by the Society to unlock it at six o'clock each morning.

By 1869 the pipe became corroded. Once again, the Society raised funds to replace the pipework, add in water from another spring and distribute it to ten standing pipes dotted about the village. This new system was welcomed by the villagers with a traditional Well Dressing.

By 1926 there were more houses to supply and a higher pressure was needed to allow taps in every home. The upgrade was achieved once again and a water treatment plant was added. Today, the village's Water Company still exists, the system complies with modern standards and water is still sourced from Bleakley Spring to 500 households and businesses in the village.

FURTHER FOUNTAINS

Bournemouth

Photograph: J L Stephenson, March 2019.

The Alum Chine fountain was built by Andrew Handysides in about 1880 and was installed in the early 1900's on the beach near Bournemouth. A 'chine' is a river valley. The fountain was made from cast iron and has had little restoration.

Andrew Handysides took over the Brittania Foundry in Derby in 1848 and brought it into the realm of fame. The Foundry made articles ranging from garden ornaments to bridges and railways and was the first to make the new standard Post Office letterboxes.

This fountain provided the thirsty traveller or tourist with fresh drinking water after their stroll on the beach.

Piazza Navona, Rome

Built on the site of an ancient Roman stadium this well-known Piazza is a beautiful light-filled square with three famous fountains. They were designed during the Papacy of Gregory XIII. In the centre there is the Fountain of the Four Rivers designed by Bernini in 1651. The statue figures represent the main rivers of the continents where Christianity had reached.

Fontana dei Quattro Fiumi (Fountain of the Four Rivers)

The Seashell Fountain changed its name to Moor Fountain when Bernini added a statue of a Moorish man wrestling with a dolphin in its centre. Finally, the Neptune Fountain dating from 1574 sports Neptune, the ancient Roman name for the God of the sea.

All these fountains were not only for offering drinking water to people and animals, but for adding beauty and grace to a public space. Until the mid-nineteenth century each summer the three fountains were allowed to overflow, so creating the 'Lake of Piazza Navona' for the amusement of the local people.

However, in a nearby side street, there is a drinking fountain of striking beauty, little seen by passers-by and is still in use today.

The 'SPQR' in the 1930's 'Triennale' type font refers to 'Senatus Populusque Romanus',

meaning 'The Roman Senate and People'. It appeared in ancient Roman political, legal and historical inscriptions. The balls (on Roman standards or flags) represented the dominion of ancient Rome over the world. The significance of the books and the deer head spouting water can be left to the imagination.

Lucca

Lucca is a small Italian city with three sets of walls – Roman, Mediaeval and Renaissance, mostly intact and expanding round each other as the city grew larger over the centuries. There are many sites and buildings of interest.

The city could thrive because in ancient times it was built in an area rich in springs and a fast-flowing stream runs through the city. It is called Il Fosso meaning stream or ditch in latin. In times of heavy rainfall its level suddenly rises and then falls again. This is due to the influence of the local springs and rivers, and the water conducted via an aqueduct from the hills. At many of Il Fosso's intersections with roads there stand public drinking fountains, where people fill up their water bottles for the hot day ahead.

Llanystumdwy, North Wales a Holy Well

A Welshman who played a large part in social reform, David Lloyd George (1863 to 1945), was a statesman, chancellor of the Exchequer and Prime Minister in England. His family came from a small village near Portmadog in North Wales. The village of Llanystumdwy lies on the old pilgrim route to the holy island of Bardsey and along the way travellers would have visited St Cybi's well for prayer and refreshment (pronounced 'St Gubby').

Here was a watercourse and wells used for the prime purpose of spiritual devotion, as well as their curative powers. It was said that the water could cure anything from blindness to warts. St Cybi lived in the area in the sixth century; the stone cottage built nearby for the caretaker was an 18th century addition. It was also used for the pilgrims to rest in, having drunk their mixture of seawater and well water to effect their cure.

St Cybi's Holy Well - the inner well, 5ft deep, inside the cottage for bathing (above), and the outer well, behind the cottage, for drinking.

The main well chamber was deep enough for bathing. The water would have felt cool and refreshing after their long haul walk. Some metres away, outside the cottage there was a well which was used or drinking, its outflow joining the main well, and from there into the stream. Holiness was mixed with practicality.

REFERENCES

Emma Jones. Parched City. Zero Books 2012. ISBN 978 1 78099 158 0

https://www.peakdistrict.gov.uk/__data/assets/pdf_file/0019/338500/bakewell-conservation-area-appraisal.pdf Accessed 18.5.19

Trevor Brighton. Bakewell: The Ancient Capital of the Peak (Halsgrove Community History) ISBN: 9781841144191. 2005.

http://www.youlgrave.org.uk/youlgrave-waterworks-ltd/ youlgreave parish website accessed 24.4.19

https://memorialdrinkingfountains.wordpress.com/2014/07/31/alum-chine-fountain/

Jones, Andrew. Every Pilgrim's Guide to Celtic Britain and Ireland. 2009. The Canterbury Press, Norfolk. ISBN 978 1 85311 453 3

H. Malchow. Free water - the public drinking fountain movement and Victorian London. p 183. 1978. Published online 18 Jul 2013.

Chapter 3 - Sustaining Supplies.

SPAS AND BATHS

Water has always served many functions – essential to life as fluid for our body's cells and structure; present in our environment and food; cleansing and cooling, and in healing. Man has experienced all of these since the very early days of his existence. A spa's water was used for its healing and health-giving properties. A few examples are outlined below.

The Baths and Washhouses Act of 1846 was designed to encourage local authorities to build washing facilities for the public in order to make it easier for people to keep clean and therefore healthier. Prior to this people did not have bathrooms or plumbing and rarely washed themselves. They had to collect clean water where they could, bring it home in buckets and heat it over an open fire. In earlier times, noble families and affluent people, like Queen Elizabeth I, washed their faces regularly and their clothes daily. She had a bath once a month, it is said, in hot water infused with herbs, 'whether she needed it or not'. This apparently was a quote from the Venetian ambassador and he meant that she took a bath even if she was not ill. The bath carried the concept of healing, especially with herbs added.

The Victorian Public Bath therefore fulfilled an important function in cleaning people and reducing the chance and spread of disease. It provided a social meeting place a little like the Roman Baths. The Washhouses offered a service where people could wash their clothes, so reducing ticks and lice. The common infection of Typhus was caused by a bacterial infection carried by lice, ticks, mites and fleas. It was associated with poverty, uncleanliness and people living closely together.

Malvern

Malvern's 'healing waters' as they became known, came from a local spring. In 1743 Dr John Wall analysed the water from this Holy Well and compared it with the waters of other Spa towns. He found it to be one of the purest as regards whether it contained 'dissolved matter'. He was one of the first four Physicians at Worcester Infirmary and used it to treat his patients there.

Spa buildings were usually impressive like this Italian one in the photograph below, at Montecatini Alto Terme in Tuscany.

The treatment included drinking this water first, then it was used to wash sores and skin conditions under running water, then covering them with damp bandages. All this makes sense in accordance with modern cleanliness. Local people and Dr Wall donated funds to improve the bathing facilities at the Holy Well. People travelled many miles to partake.

Building on this success, Malvern led the way in the new Victorian treatment of Hydrotherapy, brought to the UK in 1842 from Europe by Dr James Wilson and Dr James Manby Gully. These doctors felt that 'gentler' treatments were preferable to those using drugs like opium and they brought the Austrian idea of cold water, rigorous diet and exercise regimes. The idea of 'Hydrotherapy' or Spa treatment came to the UK, and had many followers including Darwin and Tennyson. This 'Water Cure' was in fact rather harsh, involving cold showers, wet blankets, simple diet and brisk exercise.

The idea of warm spa waters being used to ease the pain of arthritis or supporting gentle exercise in water was, in fact, used in Hippocrates' day in ancient Greece and other early civilisations. It gained popularity again in Victorian times. Today, hospitals such as Sheffield's Royal Hallamshire and the Northern General Spinal Injuries Unit have a Hydrotherapy pool staffed by Physiotherapists.

The previous two photographs are of the Spa at Montecatini Alto, Italy.

Epsom Salts – a story gone sour

In Epsom there was an underground spring in the 17th century which had a high content of magnesium. It contained a bitter-tasting mineral, magnesium sulphate (distinct from sodium chloride, common table salt). The spring was, apparently, discovered by a local cowherd on Epsom Common as he walked across it looking for water in a period of drought. He discovered that most of his thirsty cattle would not drink it. He also noted that it had a laxative effect in those which did drink it, and that sores were quicker to heal in those which waded in it. This news spread rapidly and these healing and health-giving properties were offered to the citizens of Epsom and many more. Epsom became a Spa town in the early 17th century.

The clientele drank it, bathed in it and used it to treat wounds and joint troubles. However, Epsom's spring soon dried out and people had to look for other sources. Some came from other areas in the UK and a little later an excellent source was found in the Saltworks near Cagliari (pronounced 'Calliary') in Sardinia, Italy. Seawater was collected into wide shallow lakes, the water evaporating in the heat, leaving crystals of salt (sodium chloride). These saltpans had fallen into disrepair, allowing the breeding of malaria mosquitos. It was reclaimed and turned again into a flourishing business soon after WW1. It included the production of magnesium sulphate as well by using fractional crystallisation from the seawater. So this Italian town was saved from malaria, and at the same time had a flourishing business from which the UK could also benefit.

Buxton

As far back as the Romans in AD 80, (and possibly the Celts, a thousand years before that) a warm spring was discovered in Buxton which was believed to have healing properties. The town attracted many visitors in mediaeval times for the same reason.

This beautiful, pale blue crystal-clear water bubbled up through limestone from thermal springs beneath the area of The Crescent, emerging at a constant temperature of 82°F (28°C). The Crescent was built in 1788 by the 5th Duke of Devonshire with money from his copper industry. It was a grand house with function rooms, but he gave it away to become three hotels in 1804. The guests had private entrances to the healing springs. The main benefit of the warm spring water was found in the treatment of rheumatism. This photograph is of an original tiled pool in Buxton and the reconstructed chair which was used to lower the patient into the water for hydrotherapy.

The Pump Room, which faces the Crescent, was built in 1894 and the thermal water could be taken here up until 1981. Now it is possible for the public to get Buxton water from St Anne's drinking fountain at the side of the Pump Room.

Sheffield's Turkish Bath

The first Public Baths in the city were opened on Glossop Road in 1836 following the cholera epidemic of 1832 more as a medical facility than a place of recreation. It was rebuilt from 1877 to 1879 to include a swimming pool and a Turkish Bath, the latter being traditionally a very hot and steamy experience. A ladies' bath was added in 1898 and the façade was restyled in 1908. Gradually the complex fell out of fashion, as it became common for people to have their own washing facilities at home. It eventually closed in 1990. The Turkish Baths were modernised and reopened as 'Spa 1877' in 2004 – providing a very relaxing experience.

Birley Spa, Sheffield

This Sheffield Bath House, situated in Hackenthorpe, may have been the site of a Roman Bath. Built in the late 18th century, it has since given way to what we see today. The original central bath was filled by very cold, clear water which came from an underground spring. The bath had handles for people to hold as they entered and left the water.

In 1843 Earl Manvers developed the Birley Spa building which is present today. He envisaged a large establishment with seven baths, a hotel and grottoes. The elegant house and hotel were built and attracted many visitors, mainly local people suffering from rheumatism, gout, back pain, 'general debility' and other afflictions. They did not now have to make the journey to Buxton for their treatments. Noblemen came for a bath periodically as well, such as the Duke of Portland. Hot baths were available, heated by coal fires. However, no bathing was allowed on Sundays.

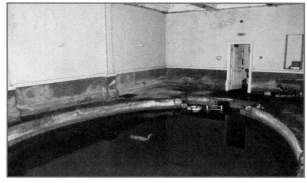

Inside Birley Spa (above) and the outside. Summer 2018. Credited with thanks to: Sheaf Valley Heritage.

Archives exist which show the expenses incurred by the owner, Robert Staniforth, but ticket sales did not cover these costs. By 1845 the enterprise was in deficit and a number of years later the hotel had closed with only one bath in operation. In 1913 it was turned into a children's pleasure garden but was forced to close when the second World War broke out and it fell into neglect. The grounds were transferred to the care of Sheffield Corporation in the 1950's.

Birley Spa circa 1844 - front view.
With permission: www.picturesheffield.com and Sheffield Archives and Local Studies Library.

Towards the end of the 20th century Birley Spa was renovated as a venue for wedding receptions and historical events. This was thanks to hard-working people who attracted Lottery funding. Interest in it fell away, however, and by 2006 it again entered a period of uncertainty. It became part of the Shire Brook Valley Local Nature Reserve.

Its future remains uncertain. The Friends of Birley Spa hope that this Grade II Listed building may be preserved for the public.

Harrogate - the Pump Room

Harrogate in North Yorkshire is a Spa town and its history as such dates back to the 16th century. William Slingsby discovered the first spring in 1571 and named it the 'Tewit Weil' Spring. It was used as a source of healing water by the travellers to and through the town.

By the late 17th century the sulphur-containing spring with its distinctive smell and taste had been discovered. It was therefore recommended for different ailments such as skin diseases and epilepsy. There is in fact a medicinal basis for the former as sulphur compounds possess antibacterial and keratolytic (skin softening) properties. When applied to skin it can help acne and some types of eczema. However, the powers of placebo and persuasion would be great for anything which tasted and smelt as pungent as this, as evidenced by my expression in the photo.

Four well heads were created in 1772 so that the water could be obtained more easily. Harrogate grew as a Spa town with its magnificent hotels and accommodation for its visitors, as well as parks and places to take exercise.

From the 1800's further spa facilities were built to meet the increasing demand. One of these was the Royal Pump Room, opened in 1842, a grand octagonal roofed building where the sulphurous water could be served in a glass, often to the music of bands. A free tap was provided outside the building for the poor who could not afford all this. There was also hydrotherapy and treatments such as 'sulphur peat baths'. The inscription 'ARX CELEBRIS FONTIBUS' graced one outer side of the building, meaning 'The Citadel of the Famous Fountains'.

The 'water cure' remained popular until the end of Victorian times. The coming of the NHS in 1948 made it unnecessary as all people regardless of their means could access medical care and more advanced treatments were being discovered. The Royal Pump Room was used as a café for a while then reopened as a museum in 1953. In 2012 the spa water, containing the largest concentration of sulphur of any spa water in Europe, was deemed unfit to drink according to an EU regulation. This was later overturned and now a visitor can taste a small sample (if they wish).

Ripon Spa and Baths, North Yorkshire

Ripon is a cathedral city in the borough of Harrogate. It is famous for its Wakeman, or Horn-blower, who has blown the city's horn each evening since the year 886 at the start of his night watch.

Ripon's Spa was the last to be opened in England.

In the early 20th century advertising the city's historical Spa took precedence. A sulphur spring nearby was discovered in 1760, but it did not become popular until the Marquis of Ripon in 1900 built a pump room and gardens. Samuel Stead designed the Art Nouveau Spa Baths in 1905, and the spa water was pumped four miles from Aldfield. A swimming bath was added in the 1930's, but the fashion for Spa treatments had passed and the Spa scheme ended in 1947. The baths remain open and the splendid tiled interior can be seen, and the original spa fountain to provide the Spa drinking water (now dry).

REFERENCES

https://www.parliament.uk/about/living-heritage/transformingsociety/towncountry/towns/tyne-and-wear-case-study/about-the-group/baths-and-wash houses/
Accessed 23.4.19

Ian Mortimer. The Time Traveller's Guide to Elizabethan England. March 1, 2012. W F Howes. ISBN 9781407497648

https://www.harrogate.gov.uk/info/20151/royal_pump_room_museum/696/history_of_the_royal_pump_room_museum

https://www.spa1877.com/about-us/history

http://staniforthfamily.com/BirleySpa.html Accessed 23.4.19

http://www.discoverripon.org/page/the_story_of_ripon.html

Chapter 4 - Sustaining Supplies

MARVELLOUS MINERAL WATERS

These magnificent clean water fountains which had rescued the population from dirt, drought and disease, fell into disdain and disrepair for reasons of lack of cash and commitment.

Bottled water first came into being as Spa water, bottled at source, and able to be sold in places remote from its manufacture. The world's bottling of water began in England in 1621, the fine water from the Malvern Hills being bottled at the Holy Well there. By the 1730's London was the centre for bottled water demand, and this special product was sold in the posh London coffee houses. There was also a growth in home brewing of 'cordial waters' at home. A cordial was so named as it was 'good for the heart'. The cordials were meant to be treatments for all kinds of common ailments, from gout to pain of childbirth, aided by the substantial quantity of alcohol in each recipe.

In 1851 Schweppes company was awarded the contract to supply free drinking water at exhibitions in Crystal Palace. This was necessarily in bottles.

Carbonated (fizzy) water was known as far back as 1767 when it was accidentally invented by Joseph Priestley (who also discovered oxygen). He found a way of dissolving carbon dioxide into water. This was used on a large scale in 1781 to produce sparkling mineral waters in bottles. The modern syphon was developed in 1829 for also dispensing fizzy water. This type of water was popular till WW2 when syphon factories were destroyed in the blitz and people had other priorities on their mind.

Wartime Water Worries

It was especially important that water was not wasted during World War II. The Metropolitan Water Board of London had a determined public awareness campaign, telling Londoners that they had a duty to value water. Water was needed to put out fires from the Blitz of the capital. Water had to be saved somehow. However, instilling new behaviour was difficult, even in the face of war.

What changed all this was in fact a natural event - that of a severe drought in 1943, which impressed in peoples' minds that water really was short. A hose pipe ban came into force and water was rationed to two gallons per person per day. The Blitz caused a total of 6000 pipes in the water network to be damaged. Tankers with water supplies were employed in damaged areas. Remarkably, no water borne disease broke out. This was on a background of the loss of nearly 30,000 people and 50,000 injured in London alone.

Lack of water played a large part in the public's thirst for other sources of drinking water, as we will see later in this chapter.

Then 'SodaStream' had a dream. The company was originally created in 1903, but in the 1970's its idea for the household was a method of making carbonated (fizzy) drinks at home. Another name was 'soda water'. A variety of fruit-flavoured syrups could be added to water and then 'fizzed' using carbon dioxide-filled small pressurised canisters. The company continues, marketing home-produced carbonated water devices, with the slogan on its website 'Turn your back on single-use plastic bottles'.

Concern over the quality of tap water began to grow with the Pollution Act of 1974. This spelled out the noxious chemicals such as fertilisers and factory effluents which should not enter the water system. In 1975 the EC Directive on Water Quality also determined the acceptable levels of lead traces and nitrates. However, people were slow to change their behaviour to save and spare this valuable resource of readily available clean water.

The year 1976 brought a severe drought due to lack of rainfall. The appearance of standpipes in the streets convinced people that something serious was going on. They became careful about how much water they used and began to appreciate every drop. When the rain finally came it carried high levels of pollution and accumulated chemicals from agricultural land into the watercourses. In particular, rural areas had an overload of nitrates in their drinking water. Babies were at added risk whether bottle or breastfed, so bottled water was made available for making up powdered milk for them.This engendered a public fear that the water was not safe for anybody, not just babies. This led to a new public scrutiny of water quality and not automatic trust.

In the late 1970's the recession began to bite. The Water Authorities' focus shifted from the fear of pollution to that of strikes. Margaret Thatcher was Prime Minister in 1979 and oversaw the compliance of the Water Authorities with the EC Directive, though this was difficult due to underfunding of the water services. They had now to test for chemicals, germs and metals in the drinking water. Further concerns were raised about water contamination with bacteria, sewage and cancer-causing chemicals in the EC Environment policy of 1981.

In 1983 the Water workforce took the decision to go on strike for equal pay with Gas and Electric workers. Once again there was desperation on the streets as water shortages were felt, leaks not repaired and standpipes reappeared. More than 20,000 homes were without water in London in February 1983. The effects of the strike were felt all over the UK. It lasted for four weeks. It resulted in a pay rise for them which was observed by the Miners' Union.

It also caused a large swing in public opinion against tap water towards that in bottles. This was the turning point for this new way of accessing the essential. Highland Spring doubled its output and Schweppes trebled the quantity of its Malvern Table Water in the shops.

In the early 1980's bottled water producers conceived the idea of a 'new drinking water'. It was advertised heavily on TV. Bottled water took on a 'healthy image' with ready portable and potable access, keeping you hydrated while exercising – for example ladies in leotards leaping about with their water bottles. It was enough to cause the publication of a book called The Good Water Guide in 1985 which furthered this new image but was correct in its assertion that, compared with sugary drinks, water is generally more healthy. At the same time, the UK adopted the EC Mineral Water Regulations which described the rules for content and labelling of the water. Several regulations were to follow as mineral waters became steadily more popular.

In 1989 England and Wales became the only countries in the world to have a fully privatised water and sewerage system. This involved the sale of the ten Regional Water Authorities to newly created privately owned companies.

Which Water Will You Want?

Nowadays the choice is fairly bewildering. The first hurdle is the difference between spring and mineral water. Both originate from an underground water table and are bottled at source. They both must be free of harmful germs and pollution. However, mineral water has to demonstrate a stable mineral composition over time, whereas spring water may vary. Mineral water is generally spring water which has had more minerals added to it at source. It is made 'sparkling' by the addition of carbon dioxide.

However, Coca-Cola's 'Dasani' water is actually USA tap water, filtered, with the addition of small quantities of sodium and magnesium. The manufactured plant-based bottles represented a 25% saving in greenhouse emissions, but producing Dasani took 2000 times more energy than producing basic tap water.

Mineral waters can be compared if one has the time. The flinty and salty-tasting San Martino of Sardinia has the highest concentration of minerals at 2,808 mg/litre (compared with Highland Spring's 216 mg/litre). It has the highest potassium content at 105mg/litre compared with zero for Buxton Water and Highland Spring. It is better described as 'Hypermineral Water' and perhaps other choices are better if a person has a kidney or cardiovascular condition.

'Bathtub Gin' as seen on the shelf in Tesco, 26.4.19

In Victorian times, a glass of gin cost less than a glass of clean drinking water.

Nowadays, the cost of a 250ml bottle of water can vary enormously, from about 0.9p per 100ml to 65p or more. This compares with the cost of tap water at 0.1p per 100ml. The costs are higher to the environment if this water is flown from another country or if non-recyclable plastic bottles are used rather than glass bottles.

The Merchant Hotel in Belfast has a water menu referred to as the Water List. (It has a Wine List as well). Water Butlers advise diners on which variety would complement their dinners, choosing from fifteen types of water from ten different countries. The mineral constituents of each are enumerated. There's no danger of allergies, but the price may cause a gasp. The most expensive is 'Iceberg Water from the Canadian Arctic Ice Shelf of Newfoundland' at £26.45 for 750ml. It is described as being 'creamy, viscous and with a textured mouth feel': perhaps tasting is believing.

Non-recyclable plastic bottles themselves are damaging to the environment but the microplastics found in bottled water itself could be damaging to human health. Scientists reporting from New York University in 2018, tested 259 individual bottles from 27 different batches across 11 brands and purchased from 19 locations in 9 countries, and found that 93% of bottled water showed some sign of microplastic contamination. It may have come from the bottling process, but further studies will be made to confirm or refute these findings.

With current annual intake of mineral water in the UK being at least 50 litres per person (and rising) and 7.7 billion single-use plastic water bottles being used, perhaps we should consider the distance that some of these bottles of water may have travelled as well as the contents.

Maybe we should return to the humble but possibly more reliable tap.

'Acqua a km zero' – it hasn't travelled to get to the table

REFERENCES

D A Simmons. Schweppes: The First 200 Years. London, Springwood Books 1983 p80. ISBN 9 780 862 54104 0

https://sodastream.co.uk Accessed 20.4.19.

Emma Jones. Parched City. Zero Books 2013. ISBN 978-1-78099-158-0

https://interestingengineering.com/study-finds-high-levels-of-microplastics-in-bottled-water

Accessed 20.4.19.

Chapter 5 - Sustaining Supplies

INGENIOUS INVENTIONS

Water is a precious resource. Its powers have been sought after by people with a mission – setting up cities, running businesses and industries, making life possible.

THE THOUGHTFUL FARMER

A farmer has a problem. How can he ensure that his herd of cows has enough water to drink especially over the drought of summer 2018? Cows require much more water than we think. For example, a cow would need between 40 and 150 litres (8 to 35 gallons) of water per day, depending on the ambient temperature, her age and whether or not she is producing milk. This means that a mixed herd of twenty cattle would need around 1,800 litres, or 400 gallons of water each day. A pig, too, would require up to 25 litres of water per day and hens are surprisingly thirsty with one average laying hen wanting at least 300 millilitres of water daily (a mugful).

A neighbour tells him that once there was a Victorian well in the orchard of his property and the farmer finds this by water dowsing. He then arranges for it to be cleared of the Victorian rubbish – broken crockery and bottles, revealing a 20 ft brick well which is fed by water draining off the surrounding fields.

He then devises a system for pumping this water up to his cattle troughs. The plan shows that he puts a pump under the surface of the water in the well, which in the space of thirty seconds, pumps the water through filters and a steriliser and control unit in a nearby barn up to a storage tank. A delayed-action float valve controls the filling of this tank, and the outflow reaches the cattle

troughs 400 yards away in about one minute.

Over the year, this clever system provides 400 cubic metres (400 tonnes) or 400,000 litres of water to the thirsty cattle. Within two years, the cost of making the system is covered by the savings in bought-in water. Clever and cow-friendly.

THE SUCCESSFUL SCIENTIST

A Physicist, also a keen vegetable gardener, lives in a thatched cottage with a long narrow garden at the bottom of which runs a small river. Many times a year there isn't enough water for the vegetable patch and the hose doesn't quite reach from the house.

He devises a type of water mill which directs water from the river up to the vegetables. He makes a 'Wirtz Pump', which uses the kinetic energy from the movement of the river water in order to raise up some water through a rotating tube. It is based on the first of its kind, invented in 1746, and works for his purposes.

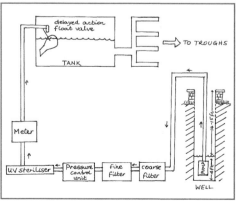

The Wirtz Pump.
Acknowledgement to Dr J H B Deane.

A similar system has been sighted in the Mediaeval garden of Perugia University, Italy.

The water wheel in the centre is moved by hand when water is required, and the containers dip into the central pond and then tip their water into the collecting troughs around the edge. I think it required quite a lot of spinning round in order to obtain enough water to use in that hot climate.

WATER FOR
WINDOW CLEANING

A window cleaning company finds that the limiting factor in the efficiency of the business is the supply of clean fresh water. A system is devised so that each window cleaner is self-sufficient, carrying two large tanks in the van, with a pumping system and a resin through which the water is passed. This removes calcium deposits and purifies the water so that it leaves no stain or 'water mark' on the glass.

This not only speeds up the process as the water feeds through the pipe to whatever height is required, but also the pure water leaves a perfectly clean window.

WATERING A
CARIBBEAN GARDEN

On the island of St Lucia there is a hotel called East Winds which comprises several small wooden traditional cottages for each of its guests. This delightful settlement is within twelve acres of tropical gardens running down the hillside. Although it has a modest annual rainfall, some months are very dry indeed.

In 2017 an irrigation system was devised whereby the Head Gardener, Sylvanus Lewis, was able to water his garden, with its 130 – 150 species of plants all year round without worrying about the weather.

'Grey' water from the laundry, kitchen, handbasins and showers is collected into a filtration plant low down in the garden, and then pumped up to the top of the hill. It is then passed through a UV filter to some holding tanks and a covered reservoir. From there it is piped to each flowerbed where it is used for watering the plants.

East Winds irrigation system holding tanks and UV filter.

FRESH FROM THE HILLS

Charles and Sarah Romanowski are justly proud of their fresh spring water, sourced in Derbyshire by sustainable means. Leam Farm (and the adjacent Leam Hall and the other nearby farms) in the Hope Valley has its own dedicated fresh spring which provides all the water needs. It has faithfully done so for 150 years, though it ran a little less in volume in the hot summer of 2018.

When the farm was built in 1758 the water must have been collected locally. The source of the water is from seven springs (the 'Seven Sisters') high on Eyam Moor. In the mid 1800's engineers from London were employed by the owners of Leam Hall to construct a water track from the springs to the hall and tied farms. They failed miserably! It took a couple of local miners from the village of Eyam to dig by hand an open track running two kilometres along the contour lines of Eyam Moor above the farm.

This open track is still functioning today and gently flows around the hilly area, down, gravity-fed, to the farm. There is a friendly community ethos to care for the waterway, which is open along all its course. All the local families have an enjoyable annual spring-clean of their stream, ensuring it does not become overgrown or damaged. Regular maintenance is needed when necessary (including pulling the occasional dead sheep from the water way and checking that moles have not dug a hole in it!)

It undergoes the statutory testing twice a year but has always been clear and clean, as it carries water from the rocky bed below the Moor. The track and its immediate environment are a wonderful area for biodiversity with ferns, mosses, frogs and small mammals.

The water track with Millstone Edge & Higger Tor in the background

Left:
Close up.
Photographs by Charles Romanowski

There is a filtration plant - a carbon filter for particles, and a UV steriliser. The farm is not connected to mains sewerage, and has a septic tank with soakaway. Charles and Sarah also have a biomass boiler that burns wood pellets and hence is carbon neutral. Therefore, Leam Farm is a cosy, sustainable home with its own dedicated supply of fresh spring water.

A MARQUEE-MAKING COMPANY ROPES IN EXPERT WATER-SAVING ADVICE

Wills Marquees near York has expanded into a new building and uses grey water to flush its toilets, together with a water treatment plant in order to make the sewerage clean. This involves a soakaway, meaning that the effluent goes into the surrounding ground after being treated rather than into the mains sewers.

This 'grey water capture' involves harvesting rain water from the roof and channelling it to an underground treatment plant (filter tank). From there it is mainly stored for the pressure washers used to clean the extensive flooring of the long main building where pristine white tent canvas is stretched and laid prior to sewing. It is fortunate that the plain of York enjoys a relatively high rainfall – its annual average is 626 mm (27 in), compared with London's 583 mm (23 in). Managing Director Christopher Brawn explains that the water re-use fits under the banner of the company's environmental policy and sustainability.

FORMER BROOMHILL METHODIST CHURCH

The former Broomhill Methodist Church in Sheffield was built in 1866. Music was so important in their worship that they had a fine three-manual and pedal organ installed. The church was built before electricity became available and so they devised a system whereby the organ was run on water power, requiring an individual conduit of water to be supplied from Redmires reservoir.

The water from the conduit was pumped under pressure in order to work bellows under the organ, allowing wind to enter and sound the organ pipes. This pressure may have varied depending on the volume of water available, so perhaps they had to choose their hymns accordingly (had I been an organist in those days, I would have been acutely aware of the effect of playing loud and quiet hymns and the available air pressure).

When electricity came (1882) the organ became electrified but the water power was still functional right up until the church was demolished in 1982.

LIGHTING THE STREETS – THE FIRST SPARK

Godalming is a historic market town in Surrey, four miles from Guildford, on the river Wey. In 1881 it became the first place in the world to have a public electricity supply and street lighting. Faraday discovered electricity in the 1820's, but it took until 1881 to light the streets. Prior to this, batteries were used – not powerful enough for street lighting.

Calder and Barnet installed an AC Alternator and dynamo in order to generate Godalming's first electricity. It was run by a waterwheel in the river Wey and was successful in lighting the streets using seven arc lights and 34 Swan incandescent bulbs. However, floods in late 1881 made the water generation difficult and it took the firm Siemens to run the system using a central distribution supply plant. However in 1884 the town voted to return to gas lighting! Reasons for this are unclear but can be imagined. Electricity generated in a more sustainable fashion returned to the town in 1904.

USE OF WATER – SHEFFIELD'S MINING

South Yorkshire's mining industry depended on water for its processes but also did battle with it. The canal system nearby allowed coalfields to develop as they were the only form of transport systems, of both personnel and product, before the railways.

Water was used to extract and wash the coal ore in the coalfield prior to transport for use elsewhere. It was also used in cooling systems, during extraction and for suppression of dust. The company needed to sustain a large supply of water for these purposes. Water was sought from groundwater, streams, rivers and lakes, or through commercial water service suppliers. A discussion was often needed between the coal mining companies and the local population.

Early settlements were built around the coalfields of which there were many in South Yorkshire. Population expansion demanded coal and coking coal for steelworks. Increasing number of mines meant that more little villages sprung up, sometimes coalescing with original ones, together with influxes of migrant workers (usually from elsewhere in the UK). Each terraced house had its own tin bath hanging outside, for use after a day's work. Water demand increased further.

The Newcomen Pump at Elsecar Colliery, near Barnsley.

Water had its drawbacks in that a mine could easily become flooded, mainly from water deep in the earth around it, or from subsidence. Powerful pumps, like this Newcomen one at Elsecar Colliery near Barnsley were needed in order to extract water which flowed into the mine shafts and in the deeper parts. The Newcomen pump, the only one in South Yorkshire, pumped water continuously from 1795 to 1923. It can now be seen as part of the Visitor Centre at Elsecar. It is the world's oldest steam engine which is still in its original location.

WINNING WATER

The Professional Groundsman has his work cut out. Rainfall is the source of much of his concern.

One local football club sought professional advice during the heatwave of June 2018 to ask about watering their pitch during the season.

They already had a tank of 15,000 litres but this wouldn't go far. There had not been any rain for four weeks. A football pitch is 7,000 square metres in size, and they had sixteen sprinklers placed around the edge and in the centre.

Working it out, 1mm of rainfall is equivalent to one litre of water volume on 1 square metre of pitch, so a pitch would need 7,000 litres.

This meant that their tank would only give 2mm over the entire pitch. They were therefore advised to water it not once but twice a day, at 11pm and at 5am, with a smaller amount. Then the water would evaporate less and the grass receive as much of the water as it could.

In a domestic lawn situation, the advice is not to water it at all in conditions of drought, as the grass becomes dormant, reviving itself when rain comes again.

WATER OF A DIFFERENT KIND – THE DYEING INDUSTRY

Potassium ammonium sulphate (called Alum), discovered by the Romans, was an essential component used in the dyeing industry. It was extracted from quarried shales, initially in Italy, and used as a fixative (mordant) for the dyeing of wool which increased the value of the cloth. It was so important to have resplendent robes that later there became a Papal monopoly on the industry. However, the Alum supply was cut off from Britain during the Reformation when King Henry VIII moved to divorce Catherine of Aragon, which angered the Pope of the time.

So Thomas Challoner set up a dyeing industry in Guisborough, North Yorkshire, moving to the coast (Ravenscar) nearby in 1640. The process for extracting alum was complex involving heating the quarried shale rock over brushwood fires for up to nine months, then leaching out the ammonium sulphate in large water-filled pits. Seaweed was then required as a source of potassium, and water of a different kind.

This essential ingredient to add to the ammonium sulphate was urine (a source of ammonia). Urine adds to the fixative and also softens the wool. At peak production this required about 200 tonnes of urine every year - the output from at least 1,000 people. The urine from Methodists was favoured as it was concentrated because they did not drink alcohol. However, as so much was required, buckets were placed in public places for any passer-by to contribute. Demand outstripped supply, and further collections had to be made from Newcastle and Hull, and as far away as London and the Orkneys. Finally, after the urine and seaweed had been added to the aluminium sulphate liquid, alum crystals settled out of it after standing for a short time.

It was probably very smelly but worth the effort. This was how the basic mordant was made for the next 250 years.

The last Alum works on the Yorkshire Coast closed in 1871. This was due to the invention of manufacturing synthetic alum in 1855, then subsequently the creation of aniline dyes which contained their own fixative, by-products of town gas works.

WATER OF A DIFFERENT KIND – THE TANNING INDUSTRY

In the first century AD, the Romans used urine in the tanning industry, even imposing a tax upon it due to its value. Urine possessed potent properties in that it dissolved fatty tissue and flesh from the inside of the hide, as well as softening it. Urine, when mixed with quicklime and wood ash, also helped to remove hair from the outside of the hide.

In the grand Estates in Britain in the eighteenth and nineteenth centuries (and possibly before), the stable boys were sent into the House to gather the chamber pots each morning, which contained the urine of the illustrious residents (and others). Morning urine was especially useful as it was relatively concentrated. They used it to clean and preserve the leather tack – bridles and saddles – of the Estate's horses.

REFERENCES

Deane, J H B. and Bevan, J J. A Hydrostatic Model of the Wirtz Pump. rspa.royalsocietypublishing.org March 28, 2018.Proc.R.Soc. A 474:2017.0533

Graham Bell. The Permaculture Garden. Permanent Publications 2004. ISBN 9781856230278

http://www.godalmingmuseum.org.uk/index.php?page=1881-godalming-and-electricity

John Briscoe. Director, GDM — building services and environmental engineers

Engineering Timelines - how to make electricity - history of public lighting

accessed 7.2.19

www.engineering-timelines.com/how/electricity/electricity_07.asp

Talk given to Sheffield branch of the History Association 7.2.19 by Melvyn Jones of Sheffield Hallam University.

Melvyn Jones. South Yorkshire Mining Villages – the history of the region's coal mining communities July 2017

Chapter 6 - Sustaining Supplies

SAVING WATER IN THE HOME

In the ebb and flow of our natural water resources, problems can be created in supply of water to our homes. Water Companies are well aware of this and can take steps to mitigate shortages in times of drought. Water can be abstracted from rivers and boreholes which makes the supply flexible, reaching areas of low flow using the underground network of pipes. Water can be moved over the whole region if needed.

What can a person do in order to conserve this precious resource when both in and out of their homes?

STOP THE DRIPS, SAVE THE DAY;
SAVE AND SPARE – THAT'S THE WAY!

Water is a precious resource for anyone at any time. Whether it is a time of drought or plenty, water needs to be used sparingly. Much energy has gone into collecting it, storing it, making it safe to drink and supplying it. Its lack of quantity and quality are keenly felt in many parts of the globe.

Tips on Tap:

- **Shower** -Instead of letting the water pour down the drain while you wait for the shower water to heat up, collect it in a bucket to use for flushing the toilet or watering the plants. Showers rather than baths take less water.

- **Tooth Brushing** -Water comes out of the average tap at 2.5 gallons per minute. Turn off the tap after you wet your brush and leave it off until rinsing.

- **Hand Washing** – some water in the handbasin is enough to wash hands, rather than under running, wasted water.

- **Fix leaks** and dripping taps – it may be a simple solution or mean calling out a plumber, but the quicker this sizeable waste is fixed, the better for everyone. Check the Water Bill each time to spot leaks which otherwise are not obvious.

- **Car Washing** - a car wash service that recycles the water, rather than washing at home with the hose, causes less to be wasted.

- **Choose efficient fixtures** - investing in a low-flow toilet, choosing efficient shower heads and opting for a Water Sense rated dishwasher and washing machine can save a lot of water in the home.

- **Consider less lawn** – grass uses much water. Instead, a xeriscaped garden could replace the lawn. This uses water-wise ground covering plants and succulents which survive on low water conditions.

Aloe vera, a succulent plant as seen growing in the Caribbean.

- **Full Loads** - Don't run the dishwasher or washing machine until full.

- **Rain Water Harvesting** – a rain barrel will collect rainwater for garden watering. There are different types available. Rain water is better for some plants as it does not contain chlorine.

- **Flush with less.** Older toilets use a lot of water. Water Companies can advise on how to reduce the amount of water used to flush different types of toilet. Putting a brick in the tank is not recommended as grit breaks off and can block pipes.

- **Use less electricity** – generation of domestic electricity uses thousands of gallons of water to cool the works. Saving on your electricity can therefore save water as well.
- **Re-use grey water** – for schemes which re-use water such as from the washing machine, seek specialist advice. Watering the garden with cooled washing-up water or bath water can help in the domestic saving programme and the soapiness is effective against greenfly.

This means that water down the plughole needn't be wasted.

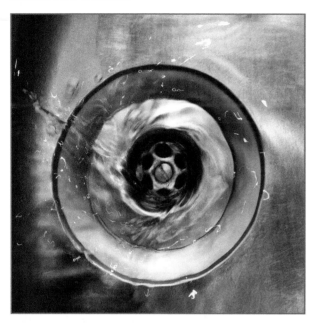

While watching it, you may see that the water eddies anti-clockwise down the hole if you live in the Northern hemisphere (as above, in Sheffield) or clockwise if you live in the Southern hemisphere. We hear about this from various sources, quoting the Coriolis effect (1835). This was initially described on a large scale, in weather systems and cyclones, but can be seen in our sinks and baths. A storm in a teacup really.

REFERENCES

https://www.nationalgeographic.org/encyclopedia/coriolis-effect/ Accessed 1.8.19.

https://www.stwater.co.uk/wonderful-on-tap/save-water/you-can-make-a-difference/

https://www.yorkshirewater.com/tips Accessed 1.8.19.

Chapter 1 - The Future for Water, the Future for Us
CLIMATE CHANGE – NO 'PLANET B'

CLIMATE CHANGE, CONCERNS AND CONSEQUENCES

What is 'climate change', including 'global warming'? What are 'greenhouse gases' and why are they damaging to our ecosystems?

The world's temperature has mostly been subject to gentle variation of about a degree Celsius up and down, but now we are seeing a definite trend of a steady increase since the industrialisation started in Victorian times. It has risen about half a degree in the past 25 years, well outside the natural cycle, and is set to rise by four degrees by the end of this century. The 20 warmest years on record have been the last 22 years, with 2015-2018 making up the top four.

This does not sound much, but even one degree increase can cause a potentially devastating rise in sea levels, ocean temperatures and acid pollution of the air which threatens the world's ability to grow crops such as wheat. This is already having an impact on our weather systems as well as on global poverty.

Millions of years ago dead plants and animals were buried and compressed and formed into fossils rich in carbon, namely coal and oil. The Victorian Industrial Revolutionaries such as Newcomen who discovered the use of coal-produced steam power were unaware of the effects on the environment. The combustion of coal releases carbon in the form of carbon dioxide (CO_2). This has continued to escalate. CO_2 is a 'greenhouse gas' which accumulates in the atmosphere and, like the glass of a greenhouse allows the sun's rays to penetrate but forms a layer which prevents escape of other pollutants such as sulphur dioxide. CO_2 levels are now at the highest level for 800,000 years. However, we need a small amount of these 'greenhouse gases' as they help to keep the earth's surface warm. This is now cycling out of control, fuelled by the polluting exhaust gases of vehicles and industries among other sources. Trees and plants use CO_2 and release oxygen which is designed to be in balance with animals who use oxygen. However, this is threatened when forests are cleared.

Another problem is brewing in the stratosphere, which is the mass of protective gases wrapped around our planet – the second layer of the earth's atmosphere. It is home to a gas called ozone (O_3) which itself is a 'greenhouse gas' but a protective one which absorbs the sun's radiation especially the harmful Ultraviolet rays (A and B). Both these can result in DNA damage in skin and cause skin cancer.

The ozone layer is being damaged and reduced by the effect of chemicals called chlorofluorocarbons (CFCs). These are found in plastics and refrigerants. The ozone layer is thinner over the poles, which is especially worrying as this will allow more of the sun's heat onto the frozen ice caps. Melting has been seen across more than half of the Greenland ice sheet during some recent summers. Melting of these 'frozen reservoirs' will cause sea levels to rise, impacting on our continents, our towns and cities and reducing the space in which an increasing population can live.

A busy town in India.
Photo: Chris and Lindsey Gill, gratefully received.

Some dead beetles were found in a cliff on the north west coast of England. They were discovered in layers denoting the era in which they died over a period of thousands of years. Russell Coope, a scientist in the mid 1960's, was able to see the effects of the prevailing climate on them. He noticed at points a sudden rather than gradual change in the temperature, denoting an Ice Age. He was proved right by subsequent testing of ice cores from Greenland.

A critical stream of seawater circulates silently. It holds the key to our global temperature. The Atlantic Conveyor is a continuous loop of water flow running around the globe, cold then warm, the latter being called the Gulf Stream. The circuit takes many centuries to complete. The warm seawater flows up from the Gulf of Mexico, past the east coast of USA and then western Europe, Cornwall and Wales. Once in the north the water cools and is added to by the melting water from the glaciers and ice sheets. This colder water then sinks and begins its long sluggish journey at the bottom of the ocean southward, meeting cold waters from the Antarctic. The mass of cold water then slides slowly north, gaining heat as it does, and slowly rising, to become the Gulf Stream again. The water as it moves, helps to give each country its particular climate.

This circulation is as fundamental as the blood circulation in an animal. It is, however, sensitive to small changes in temperature and salinity of the water. If the flood of melting ice (made of fresh not salty water) from the poles increases, the Conveyor would not become cold or dense enough to sink, and so the whole global circulation would slow down or cease. This would not cause another Ice Age, but abrupt cooling particularly of the northern hemisphere and longer winters. Scientists seem to be uncertain about the details as global warming is set to advance.

The Briksdal Glacier in Norway.

Photo from a good friend, with grateful thanks

PRESSING PREDICAMENT

What can be done in the face of this truly global challenge which makes each of us feel very vulnerable? We are not the only ones to be worried.

On 19th March 2019 Sir James Bevan, Chief Executive of the Environment Agency expressed concern that by 2050 we would be running out of water due to the dual pressures of increasing population and climate change. England is set to run short of water within 25 years. Increasing temperatures are to be expected. 'That will mean more water shortages. By 2050 the amount of water available could be reduced by 10-15% with some rivers seeing 50%-80% less water during the summer months. It will mean higher drought risk caused by the hotter drier summers and less predictable rainfall.' He advocated the building of new mega-reservoirs transferring more water across the country and setting up desalination plants to extract drinking water out of seawater.

Parched mud from the bottom of Derwent reservoir, Summer 2018

Climate Change is a problem no single country on its own can solve. However, certain agreements have been drawn up and each country has its responsibilities.

In the 1970's it was noticed that the ozone layer was thinning. This was related to the release of CFCs from fridges and sprays, so the use of these chemicals has been steadily reduced in refrigerants and aerosols, including medicines such as asthma inhalers.

The Kyoto Protocol of 1997 set emission-cutting targets for some developed countries but most failed to comply. The Paris Climate Deal of 2017, however, united all the world's nations in a single agreement to tackle climate change. (including the United States and China, which together represent almost 40% of global emissions). They agreed to keep a global temperature rise this century well below 2 degrees Celsius above pre-industrial levels.

In October 2018 the United Nations' Inter-Governmental Panel on Climate Change (IPCC) warned that governments need to make large-scale changes in order to keep global temperatures from rising over 1.5°C above pre-industrial levels. This is even more stringent than the 2 °C target of the 2015 Paris Accord, as the scientists of the IPCC felt that global warming was even more urgent a problem. Countries must cut carbon emissions by 45% by 2030 and make large cuts in greenhouse gases such as methane.

Each user of water has a part they can play in all this. Could we cut our water use by a third? Can Water Companies aim to reduce leakage from their pipes by 50 percent? Both these were advocated by Sir Bevan. He stated that the average person's daily water use of 140 litres could be cut to 100 litres in 20 years by more efficient use in home and garden. Currently, a third of precious treated water is lost to leaks or wastage. How can we reduce our water use?

Probably the one action we could take with the single largest environmental impact would be to eat less meat. We should eat less dairy produce and eat more locally sourced seasonal food, throwing less of it away. Driving electric cars would benefit (with consideration of how to generate enough electricity for everyone to have one!) and walking or cycling more. Further actions could be to take trains and buses and reduce use of aeroplanes, use videoconferencing instead of business travel, insulate homes and seek 'low carbon' on every consumer product.

A green bike seen in London outside King's Cross station, available for hire. This scheme encourages a healthy, environmentally-friendly mode of transport

REFERENCES

https://www.bgs.ac.uk/discoveringGeology/climateChange/CCS/greenhouseEffect.html Accessed 19.7.19.

https://www.nationalgeographic.org/encyclopedia/ozone-layer/ Accessed 20.7.19

https://www.gov.uk/government/speeches/escaping-the-jaws-of-death-ensuring-enough-water-in-2050 Accessed 19.7.19.

https://www.geolsoc.org.uk/en/About/History/Obituaries%202001%20onwards/Obituaries%202011/Geoffrey%20Russell%20Coope%201930-2011 Accessed 22.7.19.

Lynch, John. Wild Weather. BBC Publishing 2002.

Chapter 2 - The Future for Water, the Future for Us
SUPPLANTING PLASTIC

PLASTIC, PLASTIC EVERYWHERE

2019 saw new research coming from Bangor University, North Wales, telling us a vital story about microplastic pollution in our rivers and lakes. This contamination turns out to be far more widespread than any of us envisaged and comes as a shock. Ten sites were examined, including the river Thames, lakes in the Lake District, waterways in the Loch Lomond and Trossachs National Park, a wetland and a Welsh reservoir. Microplastics were found in all of them. The research group urges Authorities to test routinely for microplastics in water systems, not just the usual contaminants of chemical and biological pollution (see Section 1, Chapter 2). Friends of the Earth are lobbying for a change in the law to bring about an end to non-essential single-use plastic by 2025. This does not give us long.

SMALL AND DEADLY

What are Microplastics and how do they inch their way into the very water which we drink? The researchers used a fluorescence lighting system to identify and count the microplastic particles which comprise plastic fragments, fibres and film. They come from many sources - mainly from articles we use without thinking every day such as washing products (facial 'scrubs' have tiny beads of plastic added), wet wipes and tyres. Even the paints for road markings contain plastics.

Their results reveal a wide range of this contaminant from over a 1,000 pieces of plastic per litre in the river Thame in Greater Manchester to 2.4 pieces per litre in Loch Lomond.

It remains now to research further into how these microplastics reach our waterways, where they come from and what we can each do to reduce the problem.

The first plastic to be invented was a synthetic polymer made from phenol and formaldehyde in 1907 by Leo Hendrik Baekeland, a Belgian-born American chemist who also produced Bakelite. A few decades following that, plastics of many kinds were used in daily life, but their indestructible nature was not fully appreciated. Over eight billion tonnes of plastic have been produced worldwide since then and over six billion tonnes persist as waste.

Not all plastic is recyclable. Two commonly used recyclable plastics are High Density.

Discarded water bottle

Polyethylene (HDPE) and Polyethylene Terephthalate (PET)

Most plastic bottles are made from these and so can be recycled. However, much of the plastic used at present ends up in landfill because it is not currently possible to recycle it. This could be because it may be made from the non-recyclable Polyvinyl Chloride (PVC). Don't replace the lid on your water bottle before recycling, as this is generally made from PVC.

The same piece of plastic can only be recycled two or three times before its structure isn't useable any more.

Plastic in the ocean is projected to treble by 2025 threatening marine life and possibly human health according to government's scientific advisers. The Foresight Future of the Sea report covers commerce, communities and climate change among many other aspects. The total amount of plastic debris in the ocean is forecast to rise from 50 million tonnes in 2015 to 150 million tonnes by 2025. Research last year found that 90 percent of the plastic entering the ocean came from ten rivers in Asia and Africa. Bacteria such as E. coli can accumulate on plastic litter causing ill health to bathers and contaminating shellfish which have consumed tiny pieces of plastic. However, toxic chemicals being discharged into the sea poses a greater risk to life such as cadmium from industry, which is taken up by sea life. Warming of the sea is causing changes in wildlife. Coldwater fish like cod may in time be replaced by red mullet for example, due to the warming of seawater. Damage to coral reefs has been noticed for some time.

My photo of fish full of plastic bottles, made by children at Bodnant Garden Wales, 2018

Sir David Attenborough in the report 'No Time to Waste' in May 2019 reminds us that plastic pollution and rubbish are killing one person in the developing world every thirty seconds. This report by the Christian charity TEAR Fund is the first to study the impact of plastic pollution on human health. It estimates that between 400,000 and one million people die every year from diseases such as cholera, malaria and some cancers caused by living near uncollected waste and plastic pollution. A salutary fact is also that about half the world's plastic is used just once before being discarded.

The report was written in partnership with three conservation charities who call upon multinational companies Coca-Cola, PepsiCo, Unilever and Nestlé to work to reduce the amount of single-use plastics which they distribute in the under-developed world. Here, waste lies uncollected and accumulates in rivers and land near where people live.

The voices of theses charities are joined by organisations such as the National Trust which is also very concerned about plastic, encouraging beach litter-cleans along its 778 miles of coastline (quite a challenge) as well as committing to a plan to reduce reliance on single-use plastics within the charity.

In the home shopping department we now can access eco-friendly products, some plastic-free, from sites such as www.boobalou.co.uk

The purpose of Bristol's scheme, the Refill Revolution, is that the public can refill their water bottle from ten public water fountains, the locations of which are on a downloadable App. In Sheffield there is a Refill scheme where the Public can be encouraged to drink more water and waste less plastic as their water bottles can be refilled with water provided by local shops and businesses.

The Ohyo Collapsabottle, fully recyclable, made in the UK, holds 500ml and can be reused many times

Left: 800 schoolbags laid by WaterAid on the steps of St Paul's cathedral on 23.1.19 to show the number of children who die from the effects of dirty water. Each of the 24 steps represents one hour, and the 33 children under five who die every hour.
Acknowledgement: Oliver Dixon, Water Aid, with permission.

ROMA TRE UNIVERSITY – THE MESSAGE IS THE BOTTLE!

This Italian University was founded in 1992 by the Ministry of Public Education and was the third public University to be established in Rome.

It has taken a step forward when it comes to sending a message in a bottle to all its students and to the whole world. Their article, published on 9.4.19 in Corriere della Sera, told us that it has given every one of its 30,000 students a stainless steel bottle for refilling with water. They had calculated that about ten thousand plastic bottles were used each day in the University and this move would be more respectful of the environment. It was a climatic step readily embraced by the students.

REFERENCES

Redazione Roma, The Message is the Bottle. Published 9.4.19. Corriere della Sera, Rome.

https://assets.publishing.service.gov.uk/governme nt/uploads/system/uploads/attachment_data/file/ 706956/foresight-future-of-the-sea-report.pdf

https://www.recyclenow.com/recycling-knowledge/how-is-it-recycled/plastics

https://www.tearfund.org/en/media/press_releases /sir_david_attenborough_backs_new_report_revea ling_stark_health_impacts_of_plastic_pollution/

www.nationaltrust.org.uk/mag/plastics Autumn 2018.

https://www.bristolwater.co.uk/our-commuity/in-your-community/refill-revolution/

https://refill.org.uk/refill-sheffield/

www.findafountain.org

all accessed 2.7.2019

Girl by pond
by Ann Belcher

Chapter 3 - The Future for Water, the Future for Us

WEIRD WEATHER BUT CAUTIOUS OPTIMISM

WATER AND ENERGY IN THE FUTURE

There are going to be many pressures on our water and energy resources in the future. How can they be sustained? Climate change is inexorable but possibly we can do something to slow the process down. Its influence is felt most through its effect on the water cycle.

The World Energy Council in 2016 stated that ninety-eight percent of global electricity supply critically depends on the availability of water. Agriculture is the largest consumer of fresh water resources on the planet, accounting for roughly 70% of these. Food production and supply uses over a quarter of global energy, and the UN Food and Agriculture Organisation forecasts that 70% additional output will be needed to feed a 2050 global population of nine billion.

For the future of energy, water is essential. Large-scale power generation depends on there being a sustained supply of water, hydroelectricity, tidal and wave-power programmes being examples. Water also makes possible the extraction of fuels as well as cooling processes. Water itself is vulnerable to climate risk, the impact of which therefore must be urgently reduced. Power from solar and wind sources needs to be harnessed rather than the use of fossil fuels.

We can see our UK climate changing in recent years. Summers are generally hotter and tropical palm trees grow happily outside in some places. Winters no longer come bearing the blankets of snow and ice for weeks on end, and we witness tropical storms which send water down our windscreens as if from a bucket. This monsoon-like affair is counter-productive because it suddenly overloads our systems for getting rid of water, causes a huge run-off and hence flooding.

The UK has prepared for future flooding with guidance from national scientific reports in 2000 updated in 2008 and in 2016. Experience from the Dutch 'Room for the River' programme informs our flood plain expansion, and experience from Pickering in North Yorkshire underpins our creation of overflow spaces in countryside upstream of urban areas.

THE SHEFFIELD SOLUTION

Hilly Sheffield, intersected as it is by several rivers, has experience of flooding and misfortune. Flooding can have a devastating impact both on the environment and on the people who live in it. The risk of flooding is predicted to rise. The Urban Water team at Sheffield University led by Professor Richard Ashley advises the City Council about flood defences and creative ways of using land, not building on flood plains but leaving space for

A tropical storm in Barbados

A weir cleared at Hillsborough as part of the flood management work in 2009, now due for re-clearing (2019)

river waters to rise without damage. One such example is at Malin Bridge, Hillsborough where after the 2007 flood land was cleared around the rivers Loxley and Rivelin. Such sites need to take into consideration the natural wildlife and appeal to the public.

Sheffield has embarked on a £20 million flood alleviation scheme to safeguard businesses along the Lower Don valley and a £35 million scheme to build defences along the Upper Don, Porter Brook and Sheaf rivers. This may involve the building of embankments and using parks as mini-reservoirs at times of flooding. This may not be popular, but in the 2007 flood two people died and many were left homeless or without a livelihood. A compromise is needed.

The waterways running through the once industrial centre of Sheffield have made a remarkable recovery. Instead of bearing heavy contamination of toxic pollutants they are now havens of nature, thanks to the concerted efforts of volunteers on this eight-mile stretch of urban waterways comprising the river Don and the Tinsley Canal. Rubbish and litter have been picked up, invasive shrubs and plants cut back, paths cleared, and wildflower areas planted. Water flows have therefore increased and quality improved, also due to passes being made in the weirs to improve habitat for fish. Early in 2019 a salmon has been found in the river Don, the species returning after an interval of 150 years.

FLOODS, FISH AND FORTIFICATION

The" floating' Fens are situated in the south east of England, around Cambridgeshire, one of its main cities being Ely. This charming place is so called because in its early history this area was mostly covered in water, with villages on the small areas of higher ground. They resembled a community of islands, and the main source of food for the inhabitants was fish – and eels. The eel gave its name to Ely as it assumed a fundamental importance in the early civilisation: even taxes and rents were sometimes paid in eels!

There was a constant battle with water levels, as there is in Venice today. Five thousand years ago the ancient forests died and became peat and clay which held water, as well as sustaining large reed beds. However, in 1650 a large-scale drainage programme started, much against the wills of the Fenmen living there. Dutch engineers applied their engineering knowledge and much of the water was drained into the sea. The fish were no longer there as a source of food and livelihood, and the eels beat a retreat. The peat beds shrunk too, which resulted in the land and river levels dropping below that of the sea and so after a few years the river water built up as it could not drain away. Attempts were made once again to drain the Fens, this time using wind pumps driven by windmills. A more efficient job however was carried out by steam pumps of the 1820's and the Fens were drained at last.

The future with its climate change forecasts predicts problems as the sea level is likely to rise, compounding the problem of the excess water already in the area. There are small dykes punctuating the rich farmland, and over several of these there are pump houses which by radio control communicate the general water levels in the area with other pump installations. Sensors dictate when a barrier should come down to deflect or retain water flows. The management of the levels of the river Ouse in and around Ely is monitored every quarter of an hour, responding to live data from the Environment Agency.

GLIMMERS OF HOPE

'Net Zero' was a term coined by the Paris climate summit in 2015 meaning that countries would aim to deliver net-zero emissions of greenhouse gases by mid-century. This means cutting these emissions as far as we can, mainly by eliminating fossil fuel use then absorbing the remaining greenhouse gases from the atmosphere.

There are, however, signs of hope. People have invented new ideas to address this potential catastrophe and there is evidence emerging of their effectiveness.

In 2018 the UK's carbon dioxide emissions from fossil fuel use fell to a level last seen in 1890. This is due to our virtually zero use of coal and more efficient generation of energy. In 2017 more than half the electricity used in the UK came from low carbon generation – renewable and nuclear sources.

Cambridge University's Centre for Climate Change Mitigation (CCMR) has developed radical ideas to address some of the causes and effects of global warming. One of these is to spray saltwater high into the atmosphere to make the clouds more dense, in order to reflect heat back into space.

THE PLANT SOLUTION

Certain plants have become the solution to water problems in needy areas of the world. The water hyacinth is a perennial free-floating freshwater aquatic plant with thick strong waxy leaves, ballooned stem ends and is native of South America. It is considered a fast-growing weed which cause a nuisance to boats and to other plants. However, its properties of insect and disease resistance and ability to thrive in nitrogen-rich sewage-contaminated waters makes it ideal for waste water treatment and even crop production. As described in Section 4, Chapter 4 it is a plant that removes contaminants including heavy metals from waste water and so helps to prepare it for domestic use. The water hyacinth is then harvested but cannot be used as a fertiliser due to the heavy metal content but can be bio-digested to release heat and methane.

Duckweed, which is a common resident in our ponds, is a good food for fish and aquatic birds, and can thrive in very poor conditions. This makes it a good source of animal feed, such as for sheep and hens in some parts of the Third World.

Water hyacinth can also be used to form a floating platform on which to grow a number of crops. This is vitally important in areas of high flood risk such as the delta plains of Bangladesh.

Water is the most limiting factor in the production of crops for an expanding population. Crop irrigation uses more than seventy percent of available fresh water worldwide. Also, irrigated and rain fed agriculture are both affected by climate change, as it increases the risk of both intense flooding and drought. From research in Costa Rica and Nicaragua between 2012 and 2014, a system of floating crop production was born, using water hyacinth as its bed. The growth of beans, lettuce, peppers, potatoes and other essential crops depended on the nitrogen and mineral content of the water on which their bed of water hyacinth floated. Sometimes fertilisers need to be added periodically to the water, but crop yields can be enough to ensure food production in very vulnerable areas.

THE TOILET SOLUTION

A public toilet in the observatory in Jaipur, India. A communal toilet seat is considered not to be hygienic.

Photo: Chris and Lindsey Gill, gratefully received

The World Health Organisation (WHO) tells us that about 2.3 billion people still lack basic toilets. Also 4.5 billion people do not have access to safely managed sanitation which does not contaminate their drinking water.

Research efforts have been focussed on the production of toilet systems which do not require expensive mains sewerage. One solution is to extract chloride from urine, then employ electricity to obtain chlorine in order to use this as a disinfectant. Activated charcoal can remove organic material and nano-membranes can act as filters. All this could be solar powered.

Jack Sim grew up in Singapore in the 1950's and 60's and remembers having to use the communal outhouse of his village rather than owning a toilet. He is the Founder of World Toilet Day, 19th November, with the aim of inspiring action to tackle the global sanitation crisis. Toilet Twinning schemes also help to raise awareness and funds.

Most African cities only have 10-15% of households connected to mains sewerage and many urban settlements share pit latrines instead. Emptying these is a problem area, requiring workforce and funding, so research is focussing on how this sewage can be processed on site.

Lack of sanitation also has an economic impact. The Bill & Melinda Gates Foundation which has been running its Reinvent the Toilet Challenge since 2011, stated that "more than $200bn (£155bn) is lost due to healthcare costs and decreased income and productivity" as a result of poor sanitation. Inspired by this, the Government of India has embarked on the largest toilet building project in history.

GET CLEAN –
OYSTERS TO THE RESCUE

In Victorian times, oysters were very popular. They were fished regularly in all seasons and sold on the streets at four for a penny. They were often consumed there like modern 'street food', the shells being cast away. These were gathered by the urchins or street children who built them into cairns or 'grottos' and placed a candle inside, giving a pretty effect, for which the children asked for money. Mostly the shells were used by the children as begging-bowls.

This led to a stripping of this asset from the local sea beds. As well as being a sought-after delicacy, oysters perform a valuable function for the sea environment. They are biological filters. They filter about five litres of seawater per hour through their gills in order to take food (phytoplankton) from it. They are therefore susceptible to being damaged from any contaminants in the water, including microplastics. This also damages their ability to reproduce. The native oyster population in the UK has halved in the past 25 years due to this combined effect.

Researchers at Portsmouth University are well aware of the ebbs and flows of the environmental issues on their doorstep. The water quality of the Solent has fallen to low levels having an impact on the ecosystems therein, and the health of the resident fish including today's low numbers of oysters. Their project is to increase populations again by setting up protected breeding grounds, monitoring water quality and growth of the oysters. This will benefit water quality by filtering large volumes of water and removing some pollutants. The oyster beds will provide a habitat and rich food source for marine life. It is hoped that this can increase the productivity of the ecosystem, including the boosting of some fish populations which will also have an economic impact over the long term.

Let us keep in mind the surprising facts we have learnt about our water. We use most water when we eat foods such as meat. This is because it has taken a lot of water to produce this (thirsty cows and processing). Next, in our homes it is the toilet which consumes most water followed closely by the washing machine. Engaging us to be part of all this as we are consumers of water is only possible if we know a bit more about what goes on 'behind the tap'.

The key to saving our water and our world is to cut greenhouse gas emissions as far as we can. We heat our homes with gas boilers, plug in and switch on all our lights and appliances, jump in our cars without a thought of the price that the planet pays. Reducing global warming to 1.5°C means becoming no longer reliant on fossil fuels in a period of thirty years – one tenth of the amount of time it took us to reach this stage, and without compromising living standards.

Each of us can become aware of how we can push back on climate change effects, and each can make a contribution however small. Let's start by respecting and using carefully our water.

'NO MAN CAN MAKE A GREATER MISTAKE THAN HE WHO DID NOTHING BECAUSE HE HIMSELF COULD ONLY DO A LITTLE.'
EDMUND BURKE. 1729 – 1797.

REFERENCES

Floating Aquatic Plant Systems

Last Updated on Sun, 02 Sep 2018 | Wastewater Treatment

Metcalf and Eddy, Inc. (Tchobanoglous, G. and Burton, F.L). 1991. Wastewater Engineering, Treatment, Disposal, and Reuse, 3rd edition. New York: McGraw-Hill, Inc.

Ricardo Radulovich, Schery Umanzor, Rebeca Mata and Desiree Elizondo

Department of Agricultural Engineering, University of Costa Rica 90.

11 March 2015 issue of World Aquaculture Magazine.

Sharp, Liz. Reconncting People with Water – public engagement and sustainable urban water management. Earthscan (Routledge) 2017.

The Times newspaper, 8.3.18 Jim McClelland. Life-and-Death struggle for energy efficiency. Page 3.

http://uopnews.port.ac.uk/2017/04/20/portsmouth-researchers-work-with-ben-fogle-on-oyster-project-to-clean-up-the-solent/ Accessed 7.2.19

https://www.ruimtevoorderivier.nl/english/ Accessed 28.7.19.

https://www.bbc.co.uk/news/business-46289654?ns_mchannel=email&ns_source=newsdaily_newsletter&ns_campaign=NEWS_NLB_Wk47_Fri_23_Nov&ns_linkname=bbcnews_loos_newsbusiness_loos&ns_fee=0

https://www.gatesfoundation.org/What-We-Do/Global-Growth-and-Opportunity/Water-Sanitation-and-Hygiene/Reinvent-the-Toilet-Challenge-and-Expo Accessed 29.7.19.

The History
of Water